AGS

Life Skills Math

Student Workbook

by
Donald H. Jacobs
and
August V. Treff

AGS®

American Guidance Service, Inc.
Circle Pines, Minnesota 55014-1796
800-328-2560

Printed in the United States of America

ISBN 0-7854-0918-1

Product Number 90233

A 0 9 8 7 6 5

Table of Contents

How Many Calories?

Food	Calories	Food	Calories
Apple, medium	117	Chicken Breast	464
Banana	176	Egg, boiled	77
Beans, green, 1 cup	27	Hamburger, 6 oz.	270
Beef, 1 serving	214	Liver, fried, 6 oz.	390
Bread, 1 slice	63	Milk, whole, 1 cup	150
Broccoli, $\frac{2}{3}$ cup	29	Milk, chocolate, 1 cup	210
Butter, 1 tbsp.	100	Oatmeal, cooked, 1 cup	148
Cabbage, $\frac{1}{2}$ cup	20	Orange, medium	68
Cola, 12 oz.	145	Potato, baked	98
Carrots, shredded, 1 cup	42	Rice, white cooked, 1 cup	201
Cheese, 1 slice	113	Root beer, 12 oz.	150
Chicken leg	90	Steak, lean, 6 oz.	660

Directions Count the total calories for each of these meals.

1) 1 cup green beans
   2 slices bread
   1 tbsp. butter
   1 hamburger
   1 cola _____

2) 1 banana
   $\frac{1}{2}$ cup cabbage
   1 root beer
   6 oz. liver _____

3) 1 potato
   1 lean steak
   $\frac{1}{2}$ cup carrots
   1 cup milk _____

4) 1 chicken leg
   $\frac{2}{3}$ cup broccoli
   1 cup rice
   2 cups choc.
   milk _____

5) 1 steak
   2 slices bread
   $\frac{1}{2}$ cup cabbage
   1 cola _____

6) 1 chicken breast
   2 boiled eggs
   1 apple
   1 root beer _____

7) 2 boiled eggs
   6 oz. liver
   1 slice cheese
   $\frac{1}{2}$ cup cabbage
   2 apples
   1 cola _____

8) 1 serving beef
   $\frac{1}{2}$ cup cabbage
   1 cup rice
   2 bananas
   1 orange
   2 root beers _____

9) 2 potatoes
   1 cup green beans
   1 cup carrots
   1 orange
   1 milk
   1 cola _____

10) 2 cups oatmeal
    1 orange
    1 cup milk _____

11) 1 boiled egg
    2 apples
    1 cup milk _____

12) 2 lean steaks
    2 cups rice
    1 cola _____

Adding Calories

Calories Used in One Hour			
Activity	**Calories**	**Activity**	**Calories**
Lying down	75	Studying	105
Standing	125	Eating	125
Slow walking	220	Typing	140
Fast walking	300	Making beds	175
Bicycling	450	Table Tennis	230
Jogging	550	Lifting weights	500
Running	900	Sitting	100

Directions Compute the total number of calories used for each of these problems. Write your answer on the line.

1) 1 hour bicycling
2 hours jogging

_____ calories used

2) 2 hours sitting
1 hour standing

_____ calories used

3) 2 hours fast walking
2 hours eating
1 hour making beds

_____ calories used

4) 1 hour sitting
1 hour lifting weights
2 hours studying

_____ calories used

5) 1 hour running
1 hour lying down
1 hour standing

_____ calories used

6) 2 hours slow walking
3 hours table tennis
2 hours typing

_____ calories used

7) 3 hours standing
5 hours studying
1 hour lifting weights

_____ calories used

8) 1 hour eating
2 hours table tennis
1 hour bicycling

_____ calories used

9) 7 hours making beds
3 hours running
1 hour typing

_____ calories used

10) 2 hours jogging
6 hours sitting
8 hours lying down

_____ calories used

Adding and Subtracting Whole Numbers

A. Directions Write in the vertical form and add.

1) 231 + 348 + 34 + 501 = _____

2) 304 + 41 + 354 + 600 = _____

3) 4,001 + 303 + 21 + 981 = _____

4) 4,009 + 3,811 + 3,998 + 2 = _____

5) 40,098 + 21 + 50,098 + 65 = _____

6) 5,719 + 8,657 + 9,090 + 223 = _____

7) 49,946 + 9,811 + 404,042 = _____

8) 24 + 70 + 3 + 12 + 463 + 1 = _____

9) 2,538 + 8,865 + 3,342 + 220 = _____

10) 3,361 + 2,823 + 7,644 + 9,211 = _____

11) 3,947 + 6,069 + 8,558 + 222 = _____

12) 30,013 + 5,926 + 8,346 + 9,475 = _____

13) 4,059 + 33,945 + 5,673 = _____

14) 46,573 + 885,743 + 882,090 = _____

15) 488,576 + 500,546 + 3,045 = _____

16) 499,876 + 20,203 + 76,657 = _____

17) 3,994 + 1 + 223 + 475,603 = _____

18) 69,078 + 99,384 + 8,734,112 = _____

19) 388,475 + 9,948,573 + 857,643 = _____

20) 57,803 + 47,012 + 387,402 = _____

21) 399,485 + 95,043 + 4,756 = _____

22) 48,576 + 40,556 + 398,867 = _____

23) 3,049 + 30,056 + 9,908 = _____

24) 300,485 + 83,832 + 40,035 = _____

B. Directions Write in the vertical form and subtract.

1) 2,993 − 834 = _____

2) 50,677 − 9,887 = _____

3) 1,331 − 984 = _____

4) 10,023 − 5,768 = _____

5) 21,034 − 3,845 = _____

6) 48,850 − 9,886 = _____

7) 3,994 − 2,339 = _____

8) 49,500 − 35,771 = _____

9) 3,994 − 889 = _____

10) 20,034 − 3,995 = _____

11) 4,005 − 564 = _____

12) 72,234 − 20,278 = _____

13) 99,380 − 23,999 = _____

14) 49,958 − 38,838 = _____

15) 50,000 − 33,981 = _____

16) 200,341 − 98,343 = _____

17) 837,451 − 558,600 = _____

18) 22,934 − 9,988 = _____

19) 882,211 − 778,833 = _____

20) 30,000 − 7,253 = _____

21) 1,400,567 − 50,093 = _____

22) 20,230 − 8,182 = _____

Surface Area

Directions Compute the surface area for each wall. Remember to subtract the surface area for the windows and doors.

1) _____

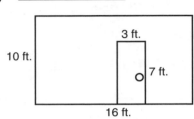

2) _____

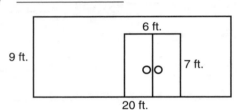

3) _____

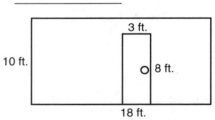

4) _____

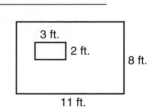

5) _____

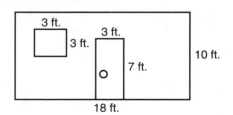

6) _____

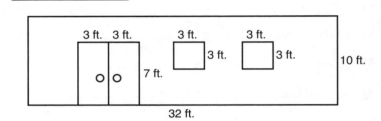

7) _____

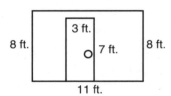

8) _____

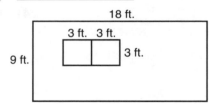

9) _____

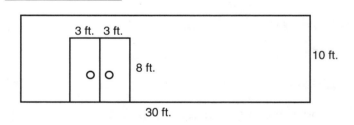

10) _____

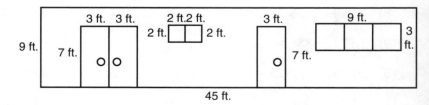

More Surface Area

Directions Find the surface area of each of these rooms. Remember to subtract the area of any doors or windows.

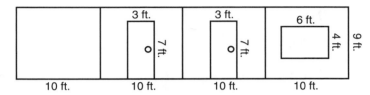

1) _____

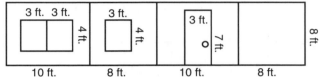

4) _____

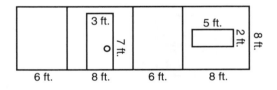

2) _____

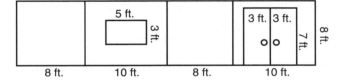

5) _____

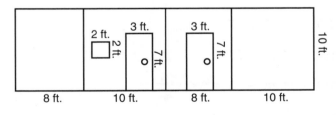

3) _____

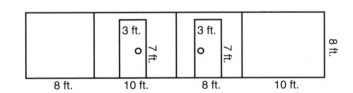

6) _____

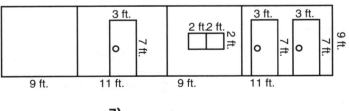

7) _____

Multiplying and Dividing Whole Numbers

A. Directions Write in the vertical form and multiply.

1) $23 \times 34 =$ _____

2) $203 \times 12 =$ _____

3) $711 \times 30 =$ _____

4) $411 \times 50 =$ _____

5) $3,001 \times 20 =$ _____

6) $2,210 \times 39 =$ _____

7) $3,004 \times 33 =$ _____

8) $2,008 \times 101 =$ _____

9) $4,003 \times 203 =$ _____

10) $9,840 \times 22 =$ _____

11) $293 \times 412 =$ _____

12) $495 \times 510 =$ _____

13) $5,006 \times 203 =$ _____

14) $9,931 \times 600 =$ _____

15) $6,324 \times 442 =$ _____

16) $8,482 \times 205 =$ _____

17) $3,004 \times 404 =$ _____

18) $9,900 \times 700 =$ _____

19) $3,945 \times 342 =$ _____

20) $8,712 \times 388 =$ _____

21) $76,301 \times 46 =$ _____

22) $20,034 \times 61,600 =$ _____

B. Directions Write in the standard form and divide. Write any
remainders as fractions.

1) $2,031 \div 5 =$ _____

2) $4,003 \div 9 =$ _____

3) $5,122 \div 8 =$ _____

4) $3,040 \div 4 =$ _____

5) $5,454 \div 7 =$ _____

6) $212,121 \div 7 =$ _____

7) $23,421 \div 11 =$ _____

8) $34,100 \div 21 =$ _____

9) $2,037 \div 22 =$ _____

10) $81,823 \div 19 =$ _____

11) $92,210 \div 31 =$ _____

12) $40,533 \div 47 =$ _____

13) $30,045 \div 25 =$ _____

14) $40,028 \div 40 =$ _____

15) $30,421 \div 67 =$ _____

16) $102,261 \div 20 =$ _____

17) $405,967 \div 50 =$ _____

18) $71,700 \div 71 =$ _____

19) $5,900,000 \div 29 =$ _____

20) $300,912 \div 91 =$ _____

21) $100,000 \div 32 =$ _____

22) $23,232,324 \div 23 =$ _____

Carpet by the Foot

Directions Carpet is sold from big rolls that are twelve feet wide.
Compute the price of carpet for each floor. The price of the
carpet is given for each floor.

1)

> 10 ft.
>
> 8 ft.

$11.95 per foot

_____

2)

> 8 ft.
>
> 7 ft.

$10.65 per foot

_____

3)

> 9 ft.
>
> 8 ft.

$12.98 per foot

_____

4)

> 12 ft.
>
> 9 ft.

$7.89 per foot

_____

5)

> 8 ft.
>
> 8 ft.

$9.36 per foot

_____

6)

> 10 ft.
>
> 9 ft.

$13.26 per foot

_____

7)

> 14 ft.
>
> 8 ft.

$10.26 per foot

_____

8)

> 6 ft.
>
> 9 ft.

$14.72 per foot

_____

9)

> 10 ft.
>
> 11 ft.

$11.54 per foot

_____

Working With Decimals

A. Directions Round these decimals to the nearer

Tenth: Hundredth: Thousandth:

1) 23.35 _____   **7)** 2.045 _____   **13)** 2.90381 _____

2) 0.0985 _____   **8)** 0.4818 _____   **14)** 47.9877 _____

3) 2.33931 _____   **9)** 3.00942 _____   **15)** 0.99981 _____

4) 89.1201 _____   **10)** 0.1919 _____   **16)** 2.2093 _____

5) 230.1 _____   **11)** 0.995 _____   **17)** 0.003321 _____

6) 90.9999 _____   **12)** 90.9999 _____   **18)** 90.9999 _____

B. Directions Compare these decimals. Use the symbol for less than ($<$)
or greater than ($>$).

1) 9.91   0.0888   **7)** 34.1   34.099

2) 0.081   0.11   **8)** 1.01010   0.991

3) 0.705   0.0999   **9)** 1.0009   1.009

4) 2.0334   3.1   **10)** 39.09801   9.9887779

5) 0.203   1   **11)** 0.9011   1.1

6) 0.9091   1.5   **12)** 40   39.9999

C. Directions Write each fraction as a decimal rounded to three places.

1) $\frac{5}{7}$ = _____   **4)** $\frac{9}{11}$ = _____   **7)** $\frac{3}{9}$ = _____   **10)** $\frac{1}{3}$ = _____

2) $\frac{7}{10}$ = _____   **5)** $\frac{8}{15}$ = _____   **8)** $\frac{3}{5}$ = _____   **11)** $\frac{6}{7}$ = _____

3) $\frac{7}{8}$ = _____   **6)** $\frac{23}{24}$ = _____   **9)** $\frac{2}{3}$ = _____   **12)** $\frac{13}{15}$ = _____

D. Directions Write each decimal as a fraction. Simplify to lowest terms.

1) 0.23 = _____   **5)** 0.855 = _____

2) 0.08 = _____   **6)** 0.005 = _____

3) 0.07 = _____   **7)** 0.05 = _____

4) 0.35 = _____   **8)** 0.4555 = _____

Life Skills Math

Adding and Subtracting Decimals

A. Directions Write in the vertical form and add.

1) 2.9 + 0.334 + 2 = _____

2) 9 + 0.43 + 2.6 = _____

3) 5.66 + 1 + 0.792 = _____

4) 0.4 + 0.594 + 8 = _____

5) 45.45 + 2.4 + 0.29 = _____

6) 3.004 + 4.5 + 8 + 0.1 = _____

7) 20.2 + 0.554 + .4 = _____

8) 231.1 + 5 + 0.586 + 0.1 = _____

9) 55 + 0.333 + 2.06 = _____

10) 2.033 + 4.4 + 6 = _____

11) 30 + 2.1 + 0.2301 = _____

12) 92.06 + 0.94 + 0.77 = _____

13) 84 + 0.46 + 2.044 + 2 = _____

14) 5.009 + 1.2 + 6.07 = _____

15) 45 + 102 + 0.4 + 5.8 = _____

16) 20.06 + 6 + 2.405 + 3 = _____

17) 304.01 + 3.0556 + 1 = _____

18) 30.99 + 3.3 + 2 = _____

19) 200.012 + 4.5 + 23 = _____

20) 50.0934 + 2.34 + 3 + 0.5 = _____

21) 33 + 405.201 + 6 + 0.2 = _____

22) 2.04 + 5 + 2.2 + 0.99112 = _____

23) 2.009 + 3.3011 + 2.9904 = _____

24) 3.009 + 4 + 67.34 + 5 = _____

B. Directions Write in the vertical form and subtract.

1) 34 − 0.56 = _____

2) 3.1 − 0.4 = _____

3) 45.2 − 0.856 = _____

4) 2.45 − 0.334 = _____

5) 5 − 0.901 = _____

6) 0.922 − 0.00234 = _____

7) 1 − 0.445 = _____

8) 2.053 − 0.995 = _____

9) 304 − 93.001 = _____

10) 9 − 3.939 = _____

11) 200 − 0.3391 = _____

12) 90 − 2.077 = _____

13) 3 − 0.901 = _____

14) 1 − 0.101 = _____

15) 23.0934 − 16.221 = _____

16) 4.3 − 2.033 = _____

17) 6 − 3.448 = _____

18) 0.00223 − 0.001998 = _____

19) 0.7364 − 0.67781 = _____

20) 2 − .2 = _____

21) 4.404 − 1.2334 = _____

22) 0.81 − 0.092 = _____

Multiplying and Dividing Decimals

A. Directions Write in the vertical form and multiply.

1) $2.3 \times 3.4 =$ _____

2) $0.34 \times 1.2 =$ _____

3) $0.29 \times 0.4 =$ _____

4) $23 \times 0.39 =$ _____

5) $83.2 \times 1.2 =$ _____

6) $38.2 \times 0.03 =$ _____

7) $22.01 \times 0.5 =$ _____

8) $40.1 \times 3 =$ _____

9) $0.992 \times 0.021 =$ _____

10) $0.402 \times .0023 =$ _____

11) $1.0023 \times 3.02 =$ _____

12) $354 \times 9.3 =$ _____

13) $0.003 \times 0.0036 =$ _____

14) $2.003 \times 0.93 =$ _____

15) $1.112 \times 2.402 =$ _____

16) $821 \times 6.3 =$ _____

17) $0.0331 \times 2.8 =$ _____

18) $4.9 \times 0.0004 =$ _____

19) $0.0003 \times 0.009 =$ _____

20) $3.3 \times 0.00009 =$ _____

21) $4.33 \times 0.22 =$ _____

22) $0.9923 \times 5.2 =$ _____

B. Directions Write in the standard form and divide. Round quotients to the nearer thousandth.

1) $348 \div 3.8 =$ _____

2) $3.4 \div 0.9 =$ _____

3) $0.35 \div 0.9 =$ _____

4) $0.27 \div 8 =$ _____

5) $7.9 \div 0.8 =$ _____

6) $5 \div .6 =$ _____

7) $1.2 \div 0.5 =$ _____

8) $6 \div 7 =$ _____

9) $34 \div 68 =$ _____

10) $2 \div 0.3 =$ _____

11) $5.02 \div 8 =$ _____

12) $7.33 \div 0.12 =$ _____

13) $0.912 \div 24 =$ _____

14) $3.55 \div 78 =$ _____

15) $22 \div 3.3 =$ _____

16) $0.00234 \div 2.2 =$ _____

17) $0.0348 \div 0.33 =$ _____

18) $8.38 \div 99 =$ _____

19) $67.3 \div 45 =$ _____

20) $6.007 \div 10 =$ _____

21) $6.401 \div 78 =$ _____

22) $445.7 \div 6.9 =$ _____

Name

Date

Period

Chapter 3

Workbook
Activity

11

Bowling

Directions Complete each frame with the correct score for each of these partial games.

1)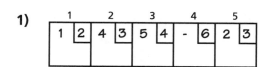

FRAME #1

2)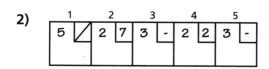

FRAME #2

3)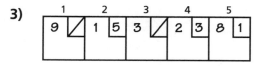

FRAME #3

4)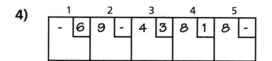

FRAME #4

5)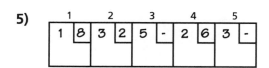

FRAME #5

6)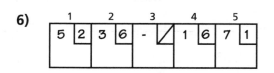

FRAME #6

7)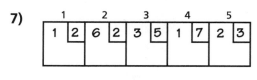

FRAME #7

8)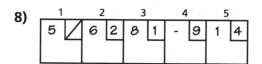

FRAME #8

9)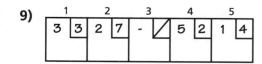

FRAME #9

10)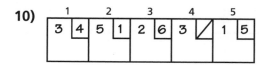

FRAME #10

11)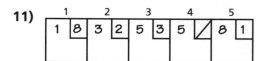

FRAME #11

12)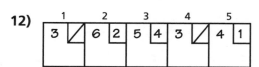

FRAME #12

13)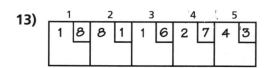

FRAME #13

14)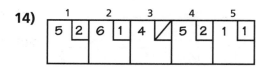

FRAME #14

Bowling Scores

Directions Complete each frame with the correct score.

1)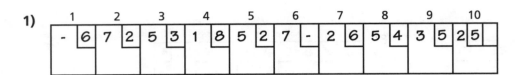

2)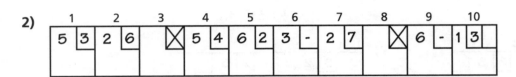

3)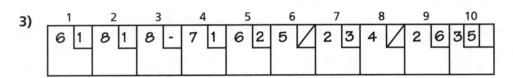

4)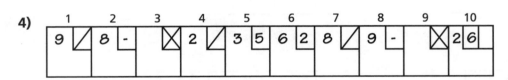

5)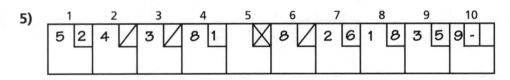

6)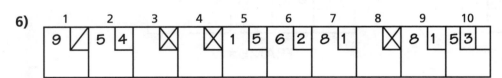

7)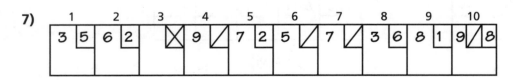

8)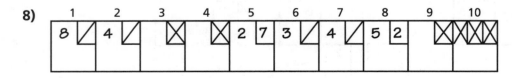

Completing Score Sheets

Directions Use the scoring information given to complete each
score sheet.

1)

1st frame:	1st roll	4		6th frame:	1st roll	3
	2d roll	5			2d roll	7
2d frame:	1st roll	3		7th frame:	1st roll	8
	2d roll	2			2d roll	2
3d frame:	1st roll	5		8th frame:	1st roll	1
	2d roll	5			2d roll	5
4th frame:	1st roll	3		9th frame:	1st roll	6
	2d roll	2			2d roll	3
5th frame:	1st roll	8		10th frame:	1st roll	4
	2d roll	1			2d roll	2

	1	2	3	4	5	6	7	8	9	10
	4 5	3 2	5 /	3 2	8 1	3 /	8 /	1 5	6 3	4 2

2)

1st frame:	1st roll	8		6th frame:	1st roll	2
	2d roll	1			2d roll	7
2d frame:	1st roll	5		7th frame:	1st roll	8
	2d roll	4			2d roll	2
3d frame:	1st roll	10		8th frame:	1st roll	9
	2d roll	—			2d roll	1
4th frame:	1st roll	0		9th frame:	1st roll	5
	2d roll	7			2d roll	4
5th frame:	1st roll	6		10th frame:	1st roll	3
	2d roll	3			2d roll	5

	1	2	3	4	5	6	7	8	9	10
	8 1	5 4	⊠	– 2	6 3	2 7	8 /	9 /	5 4	3 5

Averages

Directions Find the average. Round to the nearest tenth.

1) 34, 58, 35, 35, 33, 22 _____

2) 78, 79, 89, 83, 80, 87 _____

3) 50, 51, 51, 50, 54 _____

4) 10, 9, 4, 12, 9, 10, 6 _____

5) 40, 41, 44, 34, 60, 30, 42,
42, 45, 48 _____

6) 102, 100, 104, 105, 110,
115, 101, 111 _____

7) 9, 8, 9, 10, 20, 30, 5, 7, 8 _____

8) 11, 10, 9, 20, 10, 4, 5, 12, 33 _____

9) 94, 67, 50, 65, 83, 94, 83,
94, 83, 72, 52, 71, 70, 56 _____

10) 13, 15, 11, 18, 19, 20, 11,
12, 10, 15, 10 _____

11) 102, 100, 119, 201, 151,
100, 106, 200, 199, 101 _____

12) 100, 102, 100, 103, 101,
100, 101, 129, 132, 192 _____

13) 19, 39, 42, 73, 93, 93, 54,
62, 80, 24, 41 _____

14) 10, 64, 92, 63, 71, 64, 10,
24 _____

15) Anthony bowled a three-game set with scores of
175, 171, and 150. Compute Anthony's average score. _____

16) Marge's test scores for the first school quarter were
77, 84, 65, 80, 90, 72, 95, and 75. Solve for Marge's
quarter average. _____

17) Dean's part-time job required him to work after
school 4 hours on Monday, 2 hours on Tuesday, 2 hours
on Wednesday, and 3 hours on Friday. Compute the
average number of hours Dean worked per day. _____

18) Olivia worked a 5-day week for a total of
18 hours. Solve for the average hours she worked
per day. _____

19) Maria left at 2:00 P.M. for the beach and arrived at
6:00 P.M. If she drove 203 miles to the beach, what
was her average speed per hour? _____

20) The total attendance for the football season was
164,200. If 12 games were played, what was the average
attendance per game? _____

Vocabulary Search for Chapters 1-3

Directions Here are 24 vocabulary words. Find each word in the puzzle.
The words go across, down, and diagonally.

Addition	Computer	Menu
Area	Estimating	Paint
Average	Foot	Square
Bowling	Frame	Surface
Calculator	Graph	Wallpaper
Calorie	Height	Weight
Carpet	Length	Width
Chart	Lifting	Yard

```
F  R  X  W  G  F  T  L  T  A  W  O  G  D  G
O  Q  F  B  I  H  F  E  F  T  R  N  O  N  D
O  V  R  C  G  D  P  W  N  R  I  E  I  S  Q
T  B  L  I  A  R  T  I  L  L  A  T  A  Q  R
A  O  E  J  A  L  A  H  W  E  F  M  O  U  C
V  W  N  C  X  P  C  O  S  I  N  E  E  A  J
E  V  G  K  P  P  B  U  L  U  Y  B  M  R  R
R  O  T  G  R  A  P  H  L  Z  R  Y  R  E  N
A  B  H  H  E  I  G  H  T  A  N  F  P  F  E
G  A  X  K  D  Q  Q  W  O  O  T  A  A  I  P
E  S  T  I  M  A  T  I  N  G  P  O  R  C  T
A  D  D  I  T  I  O  N  D  L  U  O  R  R  E
C  O  M  P  U  T  E  R  L  N  L  Y  A  X  R
L  I  T  O  A  X  A  A  E  A  C  H  K  A  S
R  U  U  H  G  Y  W  M  C  C  C  O  R  I  T
```

Renaming to Lowest Terms

Directions Simplify these mixed numbers and fractions to the lowest terms.

1) $\dfrac{8}{16}$ = _____

2) $\dfrac{44}{82}$ = _____

3) $12\dfrac{8}{104}$ = _____

4) $5\dfrac{4}{20}$ = _____

5) $\dfrac{66}{92}$ = _____

6) $31\dfrac{16}{80}$ = _____

7) $2\dfrac{3}{18}$ = _____

8) $\dfrac{32}{46}$ = _____

9) $3\dfrac{3}{135}$ = _____

10) $12\dfrac{16}{30}$ = _____

11) $5\dfrac{16}{54}$ = _____

12) $11\dfrac{22}{132}$ = _____

13) $\dfrac{16}{20}$ = _____

14) $5\dfrac{10}{125}$ = _____

15) $51\dfrac{32}{96}$ = _____

16) $\dfrac{56}{60}$ = _____

17) $16\dfrac{13}{52}$ = _____

18) $\dfrac{18}{90}$ = _____

19) $\dfrac{18}{20}$ = _____

20) $3\dfrac{12}{72}$ = _____

21) $6\dfrac{5}{130}$ = _____

22) $15\dfrac{18}{20}$ = _____

23) $16\dfrac{15}{60}$ = _____

24) $\dfrac{24}{144}$ = _____

25) $33\dfrac{17}{34}$ = _____

26) $91\dfrac{81}{99}$ = _____

27) $\dfrac{33}{165}$ = _____

28) $16\dfrac{26}{44}$ = _____

29) $15\dfrac{11}{88}$ = _____

30) $2\dfrac{5}{65}$ = _____

31) $\dfrac{62}{54}$ = _____

32) $23\dfrac{7}{84}$ = _____

33) $9\dfrac{10}{35}$ = _____

34) $\dfrac{55}{66}$ = _____

35) $10\dfrac{15}{75}$ = _____

36) $3\dfrac{19}{76}$ = _____

37) $9\dfrac{18}{36}$ = _____

38) $33\dfrac{18}{54}$ = _____

39) $15\dfrac{28}{58}$ = _____

40) $5\dfrac{72}{81}$ = _____

41) $5\dfrac{6}{78}$ = _____

42) $1\dfrac{16}{66}$ = _____

43) $38\dfrac{15}{55}$ = _____

44) $13\dfrac{13}{156}$ = _____

45) $\dfrac{34}{104}$ = _____

46) $35\dfrac{18}{52}$ = _____

47) $\dfrac{16}{128}$ = _____

48) $\dfrac{26}{54}$ = _____

49) $5\dfrac{10}{62}$ = _____

50) $\dfrac{14}{70}$ = _____

51) $53\dfrac{38}{124}$ = _____

52) $\dfrac{36}{82}$ = _____

53) $\dfrac{51}{153}$ = _____

54) $\dfrac{48}{64}$ = _____

Renaming to Higher Terms

Directions Express these fractions in higher terms.

1) $\frac{2}{5} = \frac{}{25}$ _____

2) $\frac{1}{8} = \frac{}{64}$ _____

3) $\frac{5}{10} = \frac{}{60}$ _____

4) $\frac{2}{3} = \frac{}{66}$ _____

5) $\frac{17}{18} = \frac{}{54}$ _____

6) $\frac{8}{9} = \frac{}{99}$ _____

7) $\frac{2}{13} = \frac{}{52}$ _____

8) $\frac{2}{16} = \frac{}{48}$ _____

9) $\frac{6}{11} = \frac{}{121}$ _____

10) $\frac{7}{16} = \frac{}{64}$ _____

11) $\frac{1}{4} = \frac{}{52}$ _____

12) $\frac{3}{15} = \frac{}{60}$ _____

13) $\frac{11}{13} = \frac{}{65}$ _____

14) $\frac{2}{30} = \frac{}{120}$ _____

15) $\frac{6}{12} = \frac{}{96}$ _____

16) $\frac{7}{25} = \frac{}{125}$ _____

17) $\frac{3}{35} = \frac{}{105}$ _____

18) $\frac{15}{45} = \frac{}{180}$ _____

19) $\frac{3}{39} = \frac{}{156}$ _____

20) $\frac{2}{13} = \frac{}{39}$ _____

21) $\frac{5}{11} = \frac{}{132}$ _____

22) $\frac{1}{2} = \frac{}{248}$ _____

23) $\frac{17}{20} = \frac{}{1,000}$ _____

24) $\frac{6}{11} = \frac{}{66}$ _____

25) $\frac{2}{43} = \frac{}{258}$ _____

26) $\frac{2}{150} = \frac{}{900}$ _____

27) $\frac{9}{81} = \frac{}{162}$ _____

28) $\frac{5}{12} = \frac{}{36}$ _____

29) $\frac{5}{6} = \frac{}{36}$ _____

30) $\frac{5}{18} = \frac{}{72}$ _____

31) $\frac{7}{8} = \frac{}{24}$ _____

32) $\frac{7}{9} = \frac{}{72}$ _____

33) $\frac{13}{14} = \frac{}{70}$ _____

34) $\frac{7}{52} = \frac{}{156}$ _____

35) $\frac{5}{17} = \frac{}{51}$ _____

36) $\frac{2}{7} = \frac{}{84}$ _____

37) $\frac{5}{12} = \frac{}{96}$ _____

38) $\frac{2}{3} = \frac{}{57}$ _____

39) $\frac{7}{8} = \frac{}{104}$ _____

40) $\frac{1}{10} = \frac{}{1,000}$ _____

41) $\frac{11}{21} = \frac{}{147}$ _____

42) $\frac{13}{23} = \frac{}{92}$ _____

43) $\frac{9}{20} = \frac{}{120}$ _____

44) $\frac{1}{7} = \frac{}{105}$ _____

45) $\frac{1}{17} = \frac{}{102}$ _____

46) $\frac{17}{18} = \frac{}{90}$ _____

47) $\frac{2}{24} = \frac{}{96}$ _____

48) $\frac{21}{31} = \frac{}{124}$ _____

49) $\frac{2}{3} = \frac{}{222}$ _____

50) $\frac{5}{32} = \frac{}{160}$ _____

51) $\frac{29}{30} = \frac{}{210}$ _____

52) $\frac{1}{50} = \frac{}{1,000}$ _____

53) $\frac{17}{52} = \frac{}{156}$ _____

54) $\frac{51}{58} = \frac{}{116}$ _____

Playing Rummy

Directions Answer these questions about the probability of drawing the card described. Remember that the seven cards in your hand have already been drawn.

1) What is the probability of drawing a 4? _____

4) What is the probability of drawing a club? _____

2) What is the probability of drawing a 7 or an 8? _____

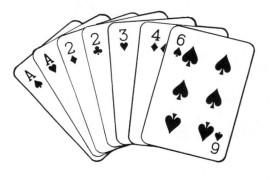

5) What is the probability of drawing a 3 or a 4? _____

3) What is the probability of drawing a 6 or a 7? _____

6) What is the probability of drawing a heart? _____

Writing Fractions

Directions Write a fraction to show what part of each figure is shaded.
Simplify each fraction to the lowest terms.

1)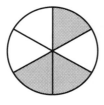
_____

2)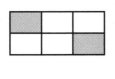
_____

3)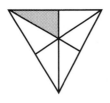
_____

4)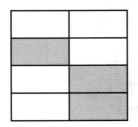
_____

5)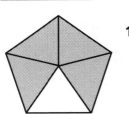
_____

6)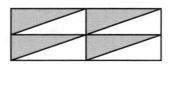
_____

7)
_____

8)
_____

9)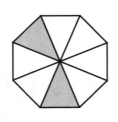
_____

10)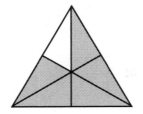
_____

11)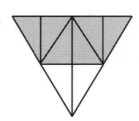
_____

12)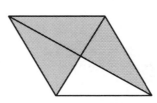
_____

13)
_____

14)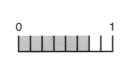
_____

15)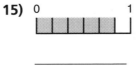
_____

16)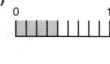
_____

17)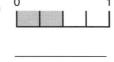
_____

18)
_____

19)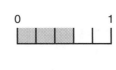
_____

20)
_____

Increasing Recipes

Directions Increase these recipes. Write your answer in the
space provided.

1) Increase to 24:

Angel Food Cake *(Serves 12)*

1 cup flour _____

$1\frac{1}{2}$ cup sugar _____

$\frac{1}{4}$ tsp. salt _____

12 egg whites _____

$1\frac{1}{4}$ tsp. cream of tartar _____

$1\frac{1}{4}$ tsp. almond extract _____

2) Increase to 36:

Basic Sponge Cake *(Serves 12)*

1 cup flour _____

1 cup self-rising flour _____

$\frac{3}{4}$ cup cornstarch _____

1 cup butter _____

1 cup sugar _____

4 large eggs _____

$\frac{1}{2}$ cup milk _____

3) Increase to 24:

Mom's Cupcakes *(Makes 12)*

1 cup flour _____

$\frac{1}{4}$ tsp. salt _____

1 tsp. baking powder _____

$\frac{1}{4}$ cup margarine _____

$\frac{3}{4}$ cup sugar _____

1 egg _____

$\frac{1}{2}$ cup milk _____

$\frac{1}{2}$ tsp. vanilla extract _____

Working With Fractions

Directions Express the following mixed numbers as improper fractions.

1) $2\frac{1}{3} =$ _____

2) $3\frac{2}{15} =$ _____

3) $3\frac{4}{33} =$ _____

4) $3\frac{2}{3} =$ _____

5) $4\frac{5}{16} =$ _____

6) $1\frac{6}{19} =$ _____

7) $3\frac{1}{4} =$ _____

8) $5\frac{6}{7} =$ _____

9) $3\frac{2}{15} =$ _____

10) $4\frac{1}{3} =$ _____

11) $6\frac{5}{12} =$ _____

12) $4\frac{1}{10} =$ _____

13) $5\frac{2}{5} =$ _____

14) $7\frac{8}{11} =$ _____

15) $2\frac{2}{13} =$ _____

16) $5\frac{2}{7} =$ _____

17) $9\frac{4}{9} =$ _____

18) $13\frac{1}{5} =$ _____

19) $6\frac{2}{5} =$ _____

20) $3\frac{6}{13} =$ _____

21) $15\frac{2}{5} =$ _____

22) $7\frac{5}{8} =$ _____

23) $5\frac{3}{11} =$ _____

24) $33\frac{1}{3} =$ _____

25) $3\frac{2}{7} =$ _____

26) $8\frac{2}{15} =$ _____

27) $11\frac{2}{5} =$ _____

28) $6\frac{1}{7} =$ _____

29) $3\frac{2}{11} =$ _____

30) $15\frac{2}{3} =$ _____

31) $8\frac{2}{5} =$ _____

32) $1\frac{5}{13} =$ _____

33) $16\frac{1}{2} =$ _____

34) $3\frac{5}{6} =$ _____

35) $2\frac{5}{22} =$ _____

36) $11\frac{2}{3} =$ _____

37) $3\frac{2}{9} =$ _____

38) $6\frac{2}{13} =$ _____

39) $15\frac{3}{8} =$ _____

40) $3\frac{5}{9} =$ _____

41) $4\frac{2}{13} =$ _____

42) $23\frac{2}{5} =$ _____

43) $8\frac{1}{5} =$ _____

44) $9\frac{2}{3} =$ _____

45) $17\frac{1}{2} =$ _____

46) $1\frac{2}{5} =$ _____

47) $9\frac{1}{4} =$ _____

48) $13\frac{2}{13} =$ _____

49) $1\frac{5}{8} =$ _____

50) $8\frac{2}{11} =$ _____

51) $15\frac{5}{9} =$ _____

52) $2\frac{5}{6} =$ _____

53) $5\frac{3}{16} =$ _____

54) $28\frac{5}{16} =$ _____

Renaming Improper Fractions

Directions Express the following improper fractions as mixed numbers.

1) $\frac{15}{5}$ = _____

2) $\frac{19}{5}$ = _____

3) $\frac{35}{34}$ = _____

4) $\frac{13}{2}$ = _____

5) $\frac{24}{16}$ = _____

6) $\frac{57}{51}$ = _____

7) $\frac{15}{7}$ = _____

8) $\frac{18}{17}$ = _____

9) $\frac{89}{17}$ = _____

10) $\frac{16}{5}$ = _____

11) $\frac{39}{5}$ = _____

12) $\frac{52}{18}$ = _____

13) $\frac{18}{3}$ = _____

14) $\frac{53}{4}$ = _____

15) $\frac{37}{32}$ = _____

16) $\frac{19}{2}$ = _____

17) $\frac{23}{8}$ = _____

18) $\frac{88}{5}$ = _____

19) $\frac{27}{4}$ = _____

20) $\frac{53}{2}$ = _____

21) $\frac{81}{80}$ = _____

22) $\frac{35}{6}$ = _____

23) $\frac{62}{8}$ = _____

24) $\frac{103}{10}$ = _____

25) $\frac{45}{3}$ = _____

26) $\frac{75}{8}$ = _____

27) $\frac{150}{70}$ = _____

28) $\frac{28}{15}$ = _____

29) $\frac{83}{11}$ = _____

30) $\frac{39}{31}$ = _____

31) $\frac{32}{7}$ = _____

32) $\frac{57}{8}$ = _____

33) $\frac{53}{7}$ = _____

34) $\frac{29}{5}$ = _____

35) $\frac{83}{5}$ = _____

36) $\frac{87}{2}$ = _____

37) $\frac{82}{10}$ = _____

38) $\frac{39}{19}$ = _____

39) $\frac{21}{4}$ = _____

40) $\frac{38}{3}$ = _____

41) $\frac{15}{4}$ = _____

42) $\frac{51}{49}$ = _____

43) $\frac{39}{15}$ = _____

44) $\frac{86}{3}$ = _____

45) $\frac{72}{9}$ = _____

46) $\frac{51}{4}$ = _____

47) $\frac{45}{2}$ = _____

48) $\frac{144}{12}$ = _____

49) $\frac{33}{6}$ = _____

50) $\frac{57}{3}$ = _____

51) $\frac{169}{12}$ = _____

52) $\frac{21}{2}$ = _____

53) $\frac{39}{15}$ = _____

54) $\frac{38}{25}$ = _____

Multiplying Fractions

Directions Multiply. Simplify the answers to the lowest terms.

1) $\frac{1}{2} \times \frac{2}{3} =$ _____

2) $\frac{5}{6} \times \frac{20}{30} =$ _____

3) $\frac{2}{5} \times \frac{15}{18} =$ _____

4) $\frac{6}{7} \times \frac{5}{6} =$ _____

5) $\frac{6}{11} \times \frac{22}{24} =$ _____

6) $\frac{3}{5} \times \frac{2}{3} =$ _____

7) $\frac{3}{11} \times \frac{33}{48} =$ _____

8) $\frac{7}{11} \times \frac{6}{21} =$ _____

9) $\frac{1}{7} \times \frac{3}{15} =$ _____

10) $\frac{3}{4} \times \frac{16}{20} =$ _____

11) $\frac{3}{17} \times \frac{9}{10} =$ _____

12) $\frac{27}{28} \times \frac{1}{9} =$ _____

13) $\frac{3}{16} \times \frac{1}{3} =$ _____

14) $\frac{4}{29} \times \frac{2}{16} =$ _____

15) $\frac{5}{21} \times \frac{7}{40} =$ _____

16) $\frac{9}{13} \times \frac{39}{54} =$ _____

17) $\frac{15}{32} \times \frac{8}{30} =$ _____

18) $\frac{5}{17} \times \frac{1}{2} =$ _____

19) $\frac{2}{5} \times \frac{10}{14} =$ _____

20) $\frac{4}{18} \times \frac{9}{16} =$ _____

21) $\frac{5}{6} \times \frac{36}{40} =$ _____

22) $\frac{2}{13} \times \frac{4}{5} =$ _____

23) $\frac{3}{8} \times \frac{1}{5} =$ _____

24) $\frac{5}{12} \times \frac{2}{7} =$ _____

25) $\frac{5}{6} \times \frac{10}{14} =$ _____

26) $\frac{4}{17} \times \frac{34}{16} =$ _____

27) $\frac{4}{17} \times \frac{3}{28} =$ _____

28) $\frac{5}{9} \times \frac{7}{45} =$ _____

29) $\frac{5}{13} \times \frac{39}{40} =$ _____

30) $\frac{5}{11} \times \frac{1}{2} =$ _____

31) $\frac{5}{12} \times \frac{1}{10} =$ _____

32) $\frac{7}{8} \times \frac{16}{20} =$ _____

33) $\frac{1}{2} \times \frac{4}{5} =$ _____

34) $\frac{8}{22} \times \frac{11}{12} =$ _____

35) $\frac{3}{4} \times \frac{8}{9} =$ _____

36) $\frac{13}{15} \times \frac{1}{10} =$ _____

Multiplying Mixed Numbers

Directions Multiply. Simplify the answers to the lowest terms.

1) $\frac{1}{2} \times 1\frac{1}{3} =$ _____

2) $\frac{5}{6} \times 1\frac{1}{5} =$ _____

3) $3\frac{2}{3} \times \frac{1}{2} =$ _____

4) $5\frac{1}{2} \times \frac{2}{11} =$ _____

5) $1\frac{1}{5} \times \frac{2}{7} =$ _____

6) $\frac{2}{7} \times 3\frac{1}{7} =$ _____

7) $1\frac{2}{13} \times \frac{13}{15} =$ _____

8) $3\frac{2}{9} \times \frac{18}{20} =$ _____

9) $\frac{5}{18} \times 2\frac{4}{7} =$ _____

10) $3\frac{2}{7} \times 1\frac{1}{2} =$ _____

11) $1\frac{2}{7} \times 1\frac{5}{9} =$ _____

12) $6\frac{1}{2} \times 6\frac{1}{2} =$ _____

13) $2\frac{1}{2} \times 1\frac{2}{9} =$ _____

14) $5\frac{1}{7} \times 4\frac{2}{6} =$ _____

15) $4\frac{2}{7} \times 1\frac{2}{5} =$ _____

16) $6\frac{2}{7} \times 1\frac{7}{11} =$ _____

17) $\frac{2}{5} \times 1\frac{2}{3} =$ _____

18) $2\frac{1}{3} \times \frac{13}{14} =$ _____

19) $\frac{2}{7} \times 2\frac{3}{9} =$ _____

20) $4\frac{2}{7} \times \frac{4}{5} =$ _____

21) $\frac{5}{8} \times 1\frac{1}{8} =$ _____

22) $\frac{8}{11} \times 3\frac{2}{3} =$ _____

23) $\frac{3}{4} \times 1\frac{1}{3} =$ _____

24) $2\frac{5}{11} \times \frac{1}{2} =$ _____

25) $2\frac{1}{2} \times 1\frac{1}{2} =$ _____

26) $4\frac{2}{3} \times 1\frac{1}{2} =$ _____

27) $2\frac{3}{8} \times 1\frac{5}{19} =$ _____

28) $2\frac{3}{4} \times 1\frac{1}{8} =$ _____

29) $2\frac{3}{11} \times 1\frac{4}{5} =$ _____

30) $1\frac{7}{8} \times 1\frac{3}{5} =$ _____

31) $3\frac{4}{13} \times 2\frac{3}{5} =$ _____

32) $3\frac{8}{9} \times 5\frac{2}{5} =$ _____

Decreasing Recipes

Directions Decrease these recipes. Write your answer in the space provided.

1) Decrease to 9:

Coconut Cookies *(Makes 36)*

1 cup flour _____

$\frac{3}{4}$ cup coconut, shredded _____

1 cup sugar _____

$\frac{1}{2}$ cup butter _____

1 cup rolled oats _____

$1\frac{1}{2}$ tsp. baking soda _____

2 tbsp. boiling water _____

2) Decrease to 12:

Butter Snaps *(Makes 24)*

1 cup butter _____

1 cup brown sugar _____

2 tsp. lemon rind, grated _____

1 egg _____

2 cups flour _____

$\frac{1}{3}$ cup chopped nuts _____

3) Decrease to 6:

Coconut Peanut Cookies *(Makes 12)*

$1\frac{1}{4}$ cup flour _____

$1\frac{1}{4}$ cup brown sugar _____

$\frac{1}{3}$ cup melted butter _____

2 eggs _____

$\frac{1}{2}$ tsp. baking powder _____

$\frac{1}{2}$ tsp. vanilla extract _____

$1\frac{1}{4}$ cup shredded coconut _____

2 cups chopped peanuts _____

Dividing Fractions

Directions Divide. Simplify the answers to the lowest terms.

1) $\frac{1}{2} \div \frac{2}{9} =$ _____

2) $\frac{4}{7} \div \frac{2}{7} =$ _____

3) $\frac{4}{9} \div \frac{2}{27} =$ _____

4) $\frac{7}{13} \div \frac{1}{2} =$ _____

5) $\frac{3}{8} \div \frac{1}{5} =$ _____

6) $\frac{4}{9} \div \frac{1}{9} =$ _____

7) $\frac{5}{6} \div \frac{2}{12} =$ _____

8) $\frac{2}{15} \div \frac{2}{5} =$ _____

9) $\frac{1}{9} \div \frac{2}{9} =$ _____

10) $\frac{5}{11} \div \frac{15}{33} =$ _____

11) $\frac{2}{3} \div \frac{5}{13} =$ _____

12) $\frac{7}{11} \div \frac{1}{15} =$ _____

13) $\frac{1}{8} \div \frac{2}{7} =$ _____

14) $\frac{3}{19} \div \frac{18}{19} =$ _____

15) $\frac{5}{16} \div \frac{2}{8} =$ _____

16) $\frac{5}{6} \div \frac{2}{25} =$ _____

17) $\frac{1}{2} \div \frac{2}{13} =$ _____

18) $\frac{5}{7} \div \frac{14}{18} =$ _____

19) $\frac{3}{5} \div \frac{15}{20} =$ _____

20) $\frac{6}{7} \div \frac{3}{14} =$ _____

21) $\frac{1}{5} \div \frac{3}{15} =$ _____

22) $\frac{4}{5} \div \frac{3}{10} =$ _____

23) $\frac{4}{11} \div \frac{1}{2} =$ _____

24) $\frac{2}{17} \div \frac{1}{2} =$ _____

25) $\frac{7}{13} \div \frac{5}{6} =$ _____

26) $\frac{4}{7} \div \frac{4}{7} =$ _____

27) $\frac{4}{7} \div \frac{8}{9} =$ _____

28) $\frac{21}{26} \div \frac{7}{13} =$ _____

29) $\frac{3}{8} \div \frac{1}{24} =$ _____

30) $\frac{2}{3} \div \frac{5}{9} =$ _____

31) $\frac{4}{7} \div \frac{1}{2} =$ _____

32) $\frac{1}{11} \div \frac{5}{22} =$ _____

33) $\frac{1}{4} \div \frac{3}{8} =$ _____

34) $\frac{3}{11} \div \frac{4}{11} =$ _____

35) $\frac{6}{7} \div \frac{8}{21} =$ _____

36) $\frac{8}{20} \div \frac{8}{10} =$ _____

Dividing With Mixed Numbers

Directions Divide. Simplify the answers to the lowest terms.

1) $\frac{5}{7} \div 1\frac{1}{7} =$ _____

2) $\frac{7}{8} \div 3\frac{2}{3} =$ _____

3) $3\frac{2}{3} \div \frac{2}{11} =$ _____

4) $\frac{1}{7} \div 2\frac{1}{7} =$ _____

5) $1\frac{1}{2} \div 2\frac{1}{4} =$ _____

6) $4\frac{1}{4} \div 1\frac{2}{5} =$ _____

7) $\frac{1}{2} \div 2\frac{1}{5} =$ _____

8) $5\frac{1}{5} \div 2\frac{3}{5} =$ _____

9) $1\frac{2}{9} \div \frac{1}{18} =$ _____

10) $4\frac{1}{2} \div 1\frac{1}{2} =$ _____

11) $\frac{2}{8} \div 1\frac{2}{5} =$ _____

12) $3\frac{1}{6} \div \frac{5}{18} =$ _____

13) $6\frac{5}{7} \div \frac{1}{7} =$ _____

14) $1\frac{2}{3} \div \frac{2}{3} =$ _____

15) $3\frac{1}{2} \div \frac{1}{16} =$ _____

16) $1\frac{2}{7} \div \frac{2}{14} =$ _____

17) $2\frac{1}{2} \div \frac{1}{2} =$ _____

18) $\frac{8}{9} \div 2\frac{5}{9} =$ _____

19) $\frac{4}{5} \div 2\frac{1}{2} =$ _____

20) $\frac{1}{5} \div 3\frac{1}{15} =$ _____

21) $3\frac{2}{3} \div 1\frac{1}{2} =$ _____

22) $1\frac{2}{7} \div 2\frac{1}{5} =$ _____

23) $2\frac{1}{7} \div \frac{1}{7} =$ _____

24) $2\frac{7}{8} \div 1\frac{1}{8} =$ _____

25) $3\frac{1}{3} \div 1\frac{2}{3} =$ _____

26) $3\frac{2}{7} \div \frac{1}{7} =$ _____

27) $5\frac{2}{7} \div \frac{1}{5} =$ _____

28) $5\frac{1}{9} \div \frac{21}{23} =$ _____

29) $9\frac{1}{8} \div \frac{42}{48} =$ _____

30) $1\frac{3}{4} \div \frac{1}{8} =$ _____

31) $5\frac{1}{8} \div \frac{1}{32} =$ _____

32) $3\frac{7}{8} \div 1\frac{1}{8} =$ _____

Using a Fabric Guide

Directions Use the fabric guide to find the amount of fabric you will need to make the garments found in the chart. Write your answer in simplest form.

Garment	Fabric Width	Misses' Sizes						
		10	12	14	16	18	20	
Top	36″	$1\frac{7}{8}$	$2\frac{1}{8}$	$2\frac{1}{8}$	$2\frac{1}{8}$	$2\frac{1}{8}$	$2\frac{1}{4}$	Yards
	45″	$1\frac{1}{4}$	$1\frac{3}{8}$	$1\frac{3}{8}$	$1\frac{5}{8}$	$1\frac{5}{8}$	$1\frac{3}{4}$	Yards
	60″	$1\frac{1}{8}$	$1\frac{1}{8}$	$1\frac{1}{8}$	$1\frac{1}{4}$	$1\frac{1}{4}$	$1\frac{1}{4}$	Yards
Skirt	36″	$1\frac{5}{8}$	$1\frac{3}{4}$	$1\frac{3}{4}$	$1\frac{3}{4}$	$1\frac{3}{4}$	$1\frac{3}{4}$	Yards
	45″	$1\frac{1}{8}$	$1\frac{3}{8}$	$1\frac{1}{2}$	$1\frac{3}{4}$	$1\frac{3}{4}$	$1\frac{3}{4}$	Yards
	60″	$\frac{7}{8}$	$\frac{7}{8}$	1	1	1	1	Yards
Pants	36″	$2\frac{1}{2}$	$2\frac{1}{2}$	$2\frac{5}{8}$	$2\frac{5}{8}$	$2\frac{5}{8}$	$2\frac{5}{8}$	Yards
	45″	$2\frac{1}{4}$	$2\frac{3}{8}$	$2\frac{5}{8}$	$2\frac{5}{8}$	$2\frac{5}{8}$	$2\frac{5}{8}$	Yards
	60″	$1\frac{3}{8}$	$1\frac{3}{8}$	$1\frac{1}{2}$	$1\frac{3}{4}$	$2\frac{1}{4}$	$2\frac{1}{4}$	Yards
Jacket	36″	$2\frac{3}{8}$	$2\frac{3}{8}$	$2\frac{1}{2}$	$2\frac{1}{2}$	$2\frac{5}{8}$	$2\frac{3}{4}$	Yards
	45″	$1\frac{7}{8}$	$1\frac{7}{8}$	$2\frac{1}{8}$	$2\frac{1}{8}$	$2\frac{1}{8}$	$2\frac{1}{4}$	Yards
	60″	$1\frac{1}{2}$	$1\frac{1}{2}$	$1\frac{1}{2}$	$1\frac{5}{8}$	$1\frac{5}{8}$	$1\frac{5}{8}$	Yards

1) 45″ fabric
size 16 top
size 16 pants

_____

2) 36″ fabric
size 10 skirt
size 12 jacket

_____

3) 45″ fabric
size 12 skirt
size 14 top

_____

4) 60″ fabric
size 16 top
size 14 pants

_____

5) 36″ fabric
size 16 pants
size 16 jacket

_____

6) 60″ fabric
size 10 top
size 12 skirt
size 12 jacket

_____

7) 45″ fabric
size 16 skirt
size 16 top
size 16 pants

_____

8) 36″ fabric
size 18 jacket
size 16 pants
size 18 top

_____

9) 36″ fabric
size 14 top
size 12 skirt
size 14 jacket

_____

10) 45″ fabric
size 14 skirt
size 16 top
size 14 pants

_____

11) 36″ fabric
size 18 jacket
size 18 skirt
size 20 pants

_____

Adding Fractions

Directions Add. Simplify the answers to the lowest terms.

1) $\dfrac{3}{16} + \dfrac{2}{16} = $ _____

2) $\dfrac{11}{18} + \dfrac{2}{18} = $ _____

3) $\dfrac{9}{11} + \dfrac{2}{11} = $ _____

4) $\dfrac{15}{18} + \dfrac{4}{18} = $ _____

5) $\dfrac{3}{8} + \dfrac{1}{8} = $ _____

6) $\dfrac{5}{21} + \dfrac{2}{21} = $ _____

7) $2\dfrac{1}{15} + \dfrac{8}{15} = $ _____

8) $8\dfrac{5}{11} + 2\dfrac{8}{11} = $ _____

9) $8\dfrac{1}{9} + 2\dfrac{3}{9} = $ _____

10) $7\dfrac{2}{18} + 3\dfrac{14}{18} = $ _____

11) $11\dfrac{5}{21} + 3\dfrac{7}{21} = $ _____

12) $2\dfrac{1}{9} + 2\dfrac{3}{9} = $ _____

13) $2\dfrac{9}{15} + 3\dfrac{8}{15} = $ _____

14) $6\dfrac{11}{13} + \dfrac{8}{13} = $ _____

15) $5\dfrac{6}{22} + 8\dfrac{20}{22} = $ _____

16) $17\dfrac{18}{25} + 2\dfrac{5}{25} = $ _____

17) $16\dfrac{18}{31} + 21\dfrac{11}{31} = $ _____

18) $10 + 2\dfrac{1}{8} = $ _____

19) $\dfrac{5}{8} + \dfrac{2}{8} = $ _____

20) $\dfrac{13}{26} + \dfrac{12}{26} = $ _____

21) $\dfrac{8}{13} + \dfrac{8}{13} = $ _____

22) $\dfrac{2}{7} + \dfrac{3}{7} = $ _____

23) $\dfrac{6}{15} + \dfrac{4}{15} = $ _____

24) $\dfrac{8}{35} + \dfrac{2}{35} = $ _____

25) $3\dfrac{2}{17} + \dfrac{16}{17} = $ _____

26) $3\dfrac{5}{16} + 2\dfrac{15}{16} = $ _____

27) $6\dfrac{1}{5} + 3\dfrac{4}{5} = $ _____

28) $15\dfrac{1}{8} + 2\dfrac{1}{8} = $ _____

29) $8\dfrac{3}{19} + 2\dfrac{5}{19} = $ _____

30) $21\dfrac{2}{25} + 5\dfrac{24}{25} = $ _____

31) $11\dfrac{5}{12} + 2\dfrac{7}{12} = $ _____

32) $2\dfrac{3}{29} + 13\dfrac{8}{29} = $ _____

33) $5\dfrac{11}{19} + 2\dfrac{15}{19} = $ _____

34) $28\dfrac{3}{7} + 2\dfrac{5}{7} = $ _____

35) $5\dfrac{17}{32} + 2\dfrac{1}{32} = $ _____

36) $33\dfrac{2}{7} + 2 = $ _____

Adding Fractions With Unlike Denominators

Directions Add. Simplify the answers to the lowest terms.

1) $\frac{2}{15} + \frac{1}{5} = $ _____

2) $\frac{5}{11} + \frac{3}{22} = $ _____

3) $\frac{3}{20} + \frac{7}{10} = $ _____

4) $\frac{8}{11} + \frac{1}{2} = $ _____

5) $\frac{4}{5} + \frac{5}{6} = $ _____

6) $18\frac{1}{9} + \frac{3}{18} = $ _____

7) $23\frac{5}{8} + 2\frac{1}{7} = $ _____

8) $13\frac{11}{18} + 2\frac{1}{36} = $ _____

9) $9\frac{2}{13} + 3\frac{18}{39} = $ _____

10) $1\frac{5}{26} + 3\frac{1}{104} = $ _____

11) $3\frac{2}{9} + 2\frac{5}{81} = $ _____

12) $15\frac{6}{35} + \frac{8}{70} = $ _____

13) $31\frac{3}{9} + 2\frac{1}{18} = $ _____

14) $10\frac{2}{11} + 5\frac{3}{13} = $ _____

15) $5\frac{3}{10} + 2\frac{5}{6} = $ _____

16) $3\frac{7}{12} + 15 = $ _____

17) $\frac{2}{3} + \frac{1}{6} = $ _____

18) $\frac{8}{12} + \frac{4}{6} = $ _____

19) $\frac{2}{9} + \frac{2}{5} = $ _____

20) $\frac{1}{6} + \frac{1}{8} = $ _____

21) $2\frac{1}{7} + \frac{15}{21} = $ _____

22) $17\frac{2}{3} + 1\frac{1}{16} = $ _____

23) $20\frac{1}{7} + 3\frac{1}{8} = $ _____

24) $25\frac{1}{5} + 1\frac{8}{11} = $ _____

25) $8\frac{6}{17} + 1\frac{5}{34} = $ _____

26) $8 + 2\frac{5}{6} = $ _____

27) $21\frac{2}{18} + 3\frac{1}{3} = $ _____

28) $14\frac{1}{2} + 2\frac{8}{15} = $ _____

29) $33\frac{2}{17} + 2\frac{1}{6} = $ _____

30) $8\frac{1}{2} + 2\frac{2}{7} = $ _____

31) $8\frac{7}{8} + 2\frac{8}{9} = $ _____

32) $9\frac{7}{8} + 2\frac{1}{10} = $ _____

Subtracting Mixed Numbers

Directions Subtract. Simplify the answers to the lowest terms.

1) $2\frac{8}{15} - \frac{3}{15} =$ _____

2) $13\frac{15}{16} - 3\frac{5}{16} =$ _____

3) $1\frac{19}{20} - \frac{5}{20} =$ _____

4) $21\frac{5}{18} - 3\frac{4}{18} =$ _____

5) $13\frac{11}{18} - 2\frac{5}{18} =$ _____

6) $11\frac{6}{7} - 5\frac{5}{7} =$ _____

7) $29\frac{15}{16} - 13 =$ _____

8) $53\frac{5}{21} - 1\frac{1}{21} =$ _____

9) $15\frac{12}{17} - 2\frac{5}{17} =$ _____

10) $32\frac{5}{7} - 8\frac{2}{7} =$ _____

11) $2\frac{33}{34} - 1\frac{15}{34} =$ _____

12) $2\frac{6}{11} - 2\frac{5}{11} =$ _____

13) $10\frac{3}{4} - 5\frac{2}{4} =$ _____

14) $3\frac{2}{7} - 2\frac{1}{7} =$ _____

15) $30\frac{7}{10} - 1\frac{2}{10} =$ _____

16) $39\frac{29}{30} - 30\frac{20}{30} =$ _____

Directions Change to common denominators and subtract. Simplify
your answers to the lowest terms.

17) $\frac{12}{13} - \frac{2}{26} =$ _____

18) $\frac{7}{8} - \frac{3}{4} =$ _____

19) $23\frac{5}{7} - 16 =$ _____

20) $18\frac{14}{15} - 5\frac{3}{5} =$ _____

21) $39\frac{5}{8} - 2\frac{2}{4} =$ _____

22) $15\frac{21}{30} - 2\frac{2}{5} =$ _____

23) $17\frac{6}{17} - 4\frac{5}{20} =$ _____

24) $10\frac{1}{2} - 2\frac{10}{31} =$ _____

25) $5\frac{6}{14} - 2\frac{1}{7} =$ _____

26) $10\frac{20}{39} - 3\frac{3}{13} =$ _____

27) $9\frac{10}{11} - 3\frac{3}{22} =$ _____

28) $5\frac{2}{3} - 4\frac{1}{9} =$ _____

29) $12\frac{8}{13} - 2\frac{1}{2} =$ _____

30) $15\frac{2}{5} - 2\frac{1}{8} =$ _____

31) $3\frac{16}{17} - 2 =$ _____

32) $5\frac{5}{11} - 1\frac{1}{3} =$ _____

Multiplication and Division of Fractions

EXAMPLE Find the area of a surface that is $\frac{2}{3}$ yd. long, and $\frac{4}{5}$ yd. wide.
Write your answer in square units. Write your answer in simplest
form.

Solution: Length × Width = Area

$\frac{2}{3}$ yd. × $\frac{4}{5}$ yd. = $\frac{8}{15}$ square yards = $\frac{8}{15}$ sq. yd.

A. Directions Find the area of each surface. Write your answer in
square units.

1) $\frac{5}{13}$ yd. × $\frac{1}{2}$ yd. = _____

2) 8 ft. × $\frac{1}{2}$ ft. = _____

3) $\frac{2}{3}$ yd. × $\frac{1}{2}$ yd. = _____

4) $\frac{7}{9}$ ft. × $\frac{2}{3}$ ft. = _____

5) $\frac{5}{6}$ yd. × $\frac{1}{2}$ yd. = _____

6) $\frac{5}{7}$ yd. × $\frac{2}{3}$ yd. = _____

7) $\frac{7}{8}$ yd. × $\frac{2}{3}$ yd. = _____

8) $\frac{8}{9}$ yd. × $\frac{1}{2}$ yd. = _____

9) $\frac{1}{2}$ in. × $\frac{1}{2}$ in. = _____

10) $\frac{4}{7}$ yd. × $\frac{2}{3}$ yd. = _____

11) $\frac{9}{10}$ in. × $\frac{1}{2}$ in. = _____

12) $\frac{3}{11}$ yd. × $\frac{2}{11}$ yd. = _____

EXAMPLE Find the length of a surface with a width of $\frac{1}{2}$ yd., and an area of
$\frac{4}{5}$ sq. yd. Write your answer in simplest form.

Solution: Area ÷ Width = Length

$\frac{4}{5}$ sq. yd. ÷ $\frac{1}{2}$ yd. =

$\frac{4}{5}$ sq. yd. × $\frac{2}{1}$ yd. = $\frac{8}{5}$ yd. = $1\frac{3}{5}$ yd.

B. Directions Find the length of each surface.

1) $\frac{5}{12}$ sq. yd. ÷ $\frac{2}{3}$ yd. = _____

2) $\frac{2}{7}$ sq. ft. ÷ $\frac{4}{5}$ ft. = _____

3) $\frac{1}{2}$ sq. yd. ÷ $\frac{1}{4}$ yd. = _____

4) $\frac{5}{12}$ sq. yd. ÷ $\frac{1}{2}$ yd. = _____

5) $\frac{3}{8}$ sq. yd. ÷ 2 yd. = _____

6) 8 sq. in. ÷ $\frac{1}{2}$ in. = _____

7) 12 sq. ft. ÷ 6 ft. = _____

8) 15 sq. yd. ÷ $\frac{3}{4}$ yd. = _____

9) 12 sq. ft. ÷ $\frac{3}{4}$ ft. = _____

10) $\frac{4}{9}$ sq. ft. ÷ $\frac{3}{5}$ ft. = _____

11) $\frac{3}{5}$ sq. ft. ÷ $\frac{1}{2}$ ft. = _____

12) $\frac{1}{2}$ sq. yd. ÷ $\frac{3}{4}$ yd. = _____

Subtracting Mixed Numbers With Renaming

Directions Change to common denominators and subtract. Rename as needed. Simplify your answers to the lowest terms.

1) $5 \; - \; 2\frac{1}{2} =$ _____

2) $18\frac{2}{3} \; - \; 3\frac{7}{8} =$ _____

3) $33\frac{5}{11} \; - \; \frac{28}{33} =$ _____

4) $39\frac{5}{6} \; - \; 5 \; =$ _____

5) $6\frac{1}{6} \; - \; 3\frac{7}{8} =$ _____

6) $18\frac{5}{13} \; - \; \frac{7}{8} =$ _____

7) $23\frac{2}{15} \; - \; \frac{17}{30} =$ _____

8) $23 \; - \; 5\frac{11}{16} =$ _____

9) $7\frac{2}{13} \; - \; \frac{1}{3} =$ _____

10) $71\frac{1}{10} \; - \; 5\frac{3}{4} =$ _____

11) $13\frac{6}{15} \; - \; 4\frac{9}{10} =$ _____

12) $3\frac{1}{16} \; - \; \frac{1}{3} =$ _____

13) $13\frac{4}{21} \; - \; 2\frac{6}{7} =$ _____

14) $11\frac{12}{13} \; - \; 5\frac{14}{15} =$ _____

15) $31 \; - \; 16\frac{5}{7} =$ _____

16) $13\frac{5}{6} \; - \; 2\frac{8}{9} =$ _____

17) $14\frac{2}{7} \; - \; 5\frac{13}{14} =$ _____

18) $39\frac{2}{15} \; - \; \frac{19}{20} =$ _____

19) $15\frac{12}{13} \; - \; 2\frac{25}{26} =$ _____

20) $1\frac{1}{5} \; - \; \frac{8}{9} =$ _____

21) $6\frac{5}{21} \; - \; \frac{2}{3} =$ _____

22) $5\frac{13}{14} \; - \; 4\frac{27}{28} =$ _____

23) $15\frac{2}{3} \; - \; 3\frac{9}{10} =$ _____

24) $19\frac{1}{9} \; - \; 17\frac{5}{7} =$ _____

25) $1\frac{1}{2} \; - \; \frac{17}{18} =$ _____

26) $4\frac{1}{9} \; - \; 2\frac{2}{7} =$ _____

27) $1 \; - \; \frac{2}{9} =$ _____

28) $10\frac{1}{16} \; - \; 5\frac{1}{5} =$ _____

29) $39\frac{1}{25} \; - \; 5\frac{1}{8} =$ _____

30) $22\frac{1}{9} \; - \; 2\frac{3}{7} =$ _____

31) $17\frac{1}{8} \; - \; 2\frac{1}{6} =$ _____

32) $23\frac{1}{15} \; - \; 3\frac{5}{6} =$ _____

Perimeter With Fractions

EXAMPLE Find the perimeter of a rectangular room with a length of $13\frac{1}{3}$ feet, and a width of $12\frac{3}{4}$ feet.

Perimeter = 2 × Length + 2 × Width

Solution: $2 \times 13\frac{1}{3} + 2 \times 12\frac{3}{4} =$

$26\frac{2}{3} + 25\frac{1}{2} = 52\frac{1}{6}$ feet

$12\frac{3}{4}$ feet

$13\frac{1}{3}$ feet

Directions Find the perimeter for each problem. Write your answer in simplest form.

1) L = $2\frac{3}{5}$ ft.

W = $1\frac{1}{5}$ ft.

Perimeter = _____

2) L = $2\frac{2}{7}$ yd.

W = $1\frac{1}{7}$ yd.

Perimeter = _____

3) L = $1\frac{5}{7}$ ft.

W = $2\frac{5}{7}$ ft.

Perimeter = _____

4) L = $8\frac{3}{10}$ yd.

W = $6\frac{1}{5}$ yd.

Perimeter = _____

5) L = $7\frac{1}{3}$ ft.

W = $6\frac{1}{7}$ ft.

Perimeter = _____

6) L = $5\frac{2}{3}$ in.

W = $6\frac{1}{5}$ in.

Perimeter = _____

7) L = $2\frac{1}{5}$ ft.

W = $3\frac{2}{7}$ ft.

Perimeter = _____

8) L = $1\frac{1}{2}$ yd.

W = $2\frac{1}{2}$ yd.

Perimeter = _____

9) L = $3\frac{2}{5}$ ft.

W = $5\frac{1}{2}$ ft.

Perimeter = _____

10) L = $3\frac{1}{2}$ in.

W = $1\frac{1}{3}$ in.

Perimeter = _____

11) L = $5\frac{2}{7}$ yd.

W = 5 yd.

Perimeter = _____

12) L = 3 in.

W = $2\frac{1}{2}$ in.

Perimeter = _____

13) L = $1\frac{1}{3}$ yd.

W = $2\frac{1}{3}$ yd.

Perimeter = _____

14) L = $2\frac{1}{6}$ yd.

W = $1\frac{1}{5}$ yd.

Perimeter = _____

15) L = 8 ft.

W = $2\frac{2}{3}$ ft.

Perimeter = _____

16) L = $3\frac{1}{2}$ yd.

W = 6 yd.

Perimeter = _____

17) L = $3\frac{2}{5}$ yd.

W = 2 yd.

Perimeter = _____

18) L = $8\frac{1}{2}$ in.

W = $2\frac{1}{2}$ in.

Perimeter = _____

Life Skills Math

Vocabulary Search for Chapters 4-7

Directions Here are 23 vocabulary words. Find each word in the puzzle.
The words go across, down, and diagonally.

Adjusting	Improper	Probability
Chance	Lowest	Product
Denominator	Macramé	Recipes
Difference	Mixed	Rectangle
Example	Numerator	Tablespoon
Factors	Outcome	Tails
Fraction	Patterns	Terms
Heads	Predictions	

M T I M P R O P E R A H Q H B

A K E M Q R K P R O D U C T F

C O F R I Z O N M T J H H X R

R R U A M X D B T I U E A H A

A T K T C S E P A S S A N S C

M V D J C T N D B B T D C G T

E D B P V O O E L M I S E P I

R T A I L S M R E V N L A A O

E Z L V I J I E S I G E I T N

C H Y D D S N W P P I X L T X

I N U M E R A T O R E A O E Y

P R E D I C T I O N S M W R O

E M Q L N Z O P N W Y P E N D

S D I F F E R E N C E L S S D

C U R E C T A N G L E E E T F R

Shopping for Food

The Hungry Food Market	
Peas, 12-oz. can. . . . . 56¢	Cat food, 6-oz. can 3/1.95
Green beans, 16-oz. can . . . . 50¢	Tuna, 6-oz. can . . . . 98¢
Corn, 12-oz. can. . . . . 49¢	Eggs, very large, doz.. . . . . 1.09
Apple juice, 48-oz. can 1.50	Dog food, 12-oz. can . . . . 95¢
Tomatoes . . . . .98/lb.	Bath soap, bar . . . . 70¢
Onions. . . . . .30/lb.	Detergent, 70-oz. box. 1.79
Pickles, 16-oz. jar . . . . 50¢	Steaks . . . . 4.89/lb.

Directions Add the prices to find the total paid for each order.

1) 2 cans peas
1 can corn
1 dozen eggs _____

2) 3 cans cat food
2 lb. tomatoes
1 lb. onions _____

3) 1 can apple juice
1 bar soap
2 cans dog food _____

4) 3 lb. onions
2 lb. steak
1 can green beans
3 cans peas _____

5) 2 cans dog food
2 lb. tomatoes
3 cans tuna
1 can apple juice _____

6) 4 jars pickles
1 box detergent
1 bar bath soap
2 lb. tomatoes _____

7) 5 lb. tomatoes
1 can apple juice
2 cans corn
2 cans peas
2 dozen eggs _____

8) 2 cans corn
2 jars pickles
3 bars bath soap
1 box detergent
1 dozen eggs _____

9) 3 dozen eggs
2 lb. steak
2 lb. onions
1 can dog food _____

10) 4 jars pickles
3 lb. tomatoes
8 cans dog food
2 dozen eggs
5 cans tuna
7 cans cat food _____

11) 2 lb. tomatoes
5 lb. onions
3 cans peas
6 lb. steak
4 bars bath soap
1 jar pickles _____

12) 5 cans cat food
7 cans apple juice
4 cans green beans
2 boxes detergent
3 cans corn
6 dozen eggs _____

13) 2 cans corn
1 box detergent
3 cans peas
5 lb. tomatoes
4 cans green beans
3 cans apple juice _____

14) 2 jars pickles
2 dozen eggs
3 cans dog food
3 cans apple juice
5 lb. tomatoes
2 lb. steak _____

15) 3 bars bath soap
2 lb. steak
1 can tuna
4 cans corn
2 dozen eggs
2 cans peas _____

Using a Map

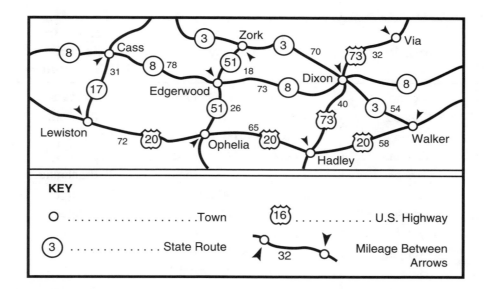

KEY

O . . . . .Town   (16) . . . . U.S. Highway

(3) . . . . State Route   Mileage Between Arrows   32

Directions Use the road map to answer these questions. Round any remainder to one decimal place.

1) How far will you drive if you go from Walker to Edgerwood along (20) and (51)?

        _____

2) If you average 51 miles per hour, how long will this trip take?

        _____

3) You drive from Cass to Hadley along (8) and (73). How far do you drive? _____

4) If this trip takes four hours, what is your average rate of speed?

        _____

5) How far is Via from Ophelia along (73) and (20)?

        _____

6) If you average 46 miles per hour, how many hours will you drive?

        _____

7) How far will you drive if you go from Lewiston to Zork along (20) and (51)?

        _____

8) To make this trip, you use 3.9 gallons of gas. How many miles do you get to the gallon of gas?

        _____

Currency Conversions

Country	Currency	Conversion Factor 1 U.S. Dollar =
Algeria	1 dinar = 100 centimes	4.93 dinars
Canada	1 dollar = 100 cents	1.08 dollars
Chile	1 peso = 100 centavos	3.5 pesos
Ghana	1 cedi = 100 pesewas	1.02 cedis
Greece	1 drachma = 100 lepta	30 drachmas
Iceland	1 krona = 100 aurar	88 kronas
India	1 rupee = 100 paise	7.5 rupees
Myanmar	1 kyat = 100 pyas	4.76 kyats
Kenya	1 shilling = 100 cents	7.14 shillings
Russia	1 ruble = 100 kopecks	.9 rubles
Zambia	1 kwacha = 100 ngwee	.71 kwachas

Directions Use the currency conversion chart to make these conversions.
Round any remainders to two decimal places.

1) Change 45 Canadian dollars to U.S. currency. _____

2) Change 78 Greek drachmas to U.S. currency. _____

3) Change 50 U.S. dollars to rupees. _____

4) Change 60 Algerian dinars to U.S. currency. _____

5) Change 72 U.S. dollars to cedis. _____

6) Change 106 kyats to U.S. currency. _____

7) Change 96 U.S. dollars to rubles. _____

8) Change 45 U.S. dollars to pesos. _____

9) Change 50 kronas to U.S. currency. _____

10) Change 62 Kenyan shillings to U.S. currency. _____

11) Change 180 U.S. dollars to kronas. _____

12) Change 180 U.S. dollars to kwachas. _____

13) Change 136 pesos to U.S. currency. _____

14) Change 93 U.S. dollars to rubles. _____

15) Change 142 U.S. dollars to shillings. _____

16) Change 37 kwachas to U.S. currency. _____

17) Change 52 kyats to U.S. currency. _____

18) Change 26 U.S. dollars to dinars. _____

Set the Time

Directions Draw the clock hands to match the time given.

1)
1:15

7)
1:35

13)
3:18

19)
9:50

2)
2:30

8)
10:25

14)
6:10

20)
12:55

3)
11:45

9)
5:03

15)
1:10

21)
3:22

4)
7:23

10)
7:05

16)
8:12

22)
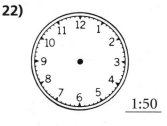
1:50

5)
3:40

11)
12:10

17)
1:58

23)
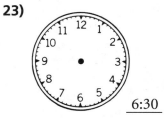
6:30

6)
9:00

12)
4:55

18)
12:22

24)
4:40

Tell the Time

Directions Write the correct time in the space provided.

1)  _____

2)  _____

3)  _____

4)  _____

5)  _____

6)  _____

7)  _____

8)  _____

9)  _____

10)  _____

11)  _____

12)  _____

13)  _____

14)  _____

15)  _____

16)  _____

17)  _____

18) 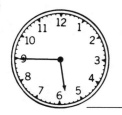 _____

19)  _____

20)  _____

21)  _____

22)  _____

23)  _____

24)  _____

Elapsed Time

Directions Subtract to find how much time has elapsed from the time
shown on clock A to the time shown on clock B.

	A	B			A	B

1)
_____

5)
_____

2)
_____

6)
_____

3)
_____

7)
_____

4)
_____

8)

_____

Clock Watching

Directions   Answer these questions about time. The clock to the right of each problem shows the current time.

1) The *Tuesday Afternoon Movie* comes on at 4:30. How long must we wait?

_____

2) The *Chester Frump Show* started at 8:30. How much of the show did we miss?

_____

3) You put enough money in the parking meter for one hour and fifteen minutes. By what time must you return?

_____

4) The umpire stopped the game at 6:32 because of rain. The game has just resumed. How long was the delay?

_____

5) You are to bake the turkey for three hours and fifteen minutes. At what time will it be finished baking?

_____

6) The boat is scheduled to arrive at 7:09. How much time is left before the boat arrives?

_____

7) The train is scheduled to leave at 8:17. How much time is left before the train leaves?

_____

8) The party starts at 9:00. How much time is left before the party begins?

_____

9) Barbara goes to sleep at 10:42 at night. When she wakes up in the morning, she looks at the clock. How long has she slept?

_____

10) Juanita gets to the doctor's office at 12:10. She looks at her watch when her name is finally called. How long has she waited?

_____

Vocabulary Search for Chapters 8-11

Directions Here are 23 vocabulary words. Find each word in the puzzle.
The words go across, down, and diagonally.

Annual	Hour	Premium
Baseball	Liter	Prices
Consumption	Money	Rates
Decimals	Odometer	Reading
Double	Overtime	Schedules
Elapsed	Pay	Spending
Gallon	Per	Value
Gross	Place	

U	A	Q	K	G	C	Q	C	O	Y	P	K	K	C	H
A	I	M	P	I	A	E	P	E	R	S	B	P	O	H
F	W	S	Y	R	L	L	N	R	A	T	E	S	N	T
F	G	O	C	B	E	O	L	P	C	S	I	P	S	T
C	E	L	U	H	M	M	Z	O	L	F	L	E	U	Q
G	R	O	S	S	E	I	I	A	N	A	H	R	M	T
B	D	R	Q	X	W	D	M	U	U	Y	O	O	P	Y
N	A	S	E	G	Q	I	U	N	M	K	V	D	T	X
M	L	S	P	A	C	T	N	L	R	P	E	O	I	I
N	H	J	E	E	D	A	D	X	E	R	R	M	O	V
H	O	V	D	B	N	I	Q	I	E	S	T	E	N	P
R	U	P	A	Y	A	D	N	T	E	N	I	T	M	L
P	R	I	C	E	S	L	I	G	V	E	M	E	W	A
V	A	L	U	E	L	L	L	N	U	A	E	R	Q	C
E	L	A	P	S	E	D	K	O	G	H	T	U	I	E

Batting Averages

Directions Find each player's batting average. Round any remainder to three decimal places.

1) Ronni Dixon
36 at bats
27 hits

_____

2) Al Geor
40 at bats
17 hits

_____

3) Tom Proveaux
24 at bats
18 hits

_____

4) John Gaines
28 at bats
18 hits

_____

5) Sam Billups
48 at bats
42 hits

_____

6) Jim Griffin
23 at bats
11 hits

_____

7) Marve Teaberry
32 at bats
24 hits

_____

8) Connie Forte
27 at bats
19 hits

_____

9) Joe Parker
16 at bats
8 hits

_____

10) Barry Chase
33 at bats
12 hits

_____

11) Marilyn Rondeau
15 at bats
9 hits

_____

12) Jane Greystoke
41 at bats
16 hits

_____

13) Chris Snee
62 at bats
21 hits

_____

14) Sam Simon
54 at bats
17 hits

_____

15) Gene Lehman
64 at bats
46 hits

_____

16) Juan Edgerton
72 at bats
44 hits

_____

17) Tish Weise
56 at bats
42 hits

_____

18) Ann Lemon
73 at bats
16 hits

_____

Slugging Percentages

Directions Find the slugging percentage for each player. Remember,
walks and sacrifices do not count as official at bats. Round
any remainder to three decimal places.

1) *Barbara Via*
2 home runs
1 triple
5 doubles
18 singles
7 walks
20 outs
9 sacrifices

_____

2) *Cal Luckett*
1 home run
2 triples
6 doubles
10 singles
3 walks
24 outs
12 sacrifices

_____

3) *Jim Kramer*
3 home runs
0 triples
2 doubles
8 singles
9 walks
7 outs
14 sacrifices

_____

4) *Mikey Rouse*
4 home runs
2 triples
3 doubles
7 singles
6 walks
11 outs
6 sacrifices

_____

5) *Don Dalk*
10 home runs
6 triples
8 doubles
0 singles
10 walks
17 outs
10 sacrifices

_____

6) *Manny Moose*
3 home runs
0 triples
3 doubles
8 singles
4 walks
8 outs
16 sacrifices

_____

7) *Susan Henning*
0 home runs
4 triples
7 doubles
11 singles
10 walks
3 outs
3 sacrifices

_____

8) *Joan Jones*
3 home runs
6 triples
12 doubles
8 singles
9 walks
8 outs
9 sacrifices

_____

9) *Rob Rees*
6 home runs
2 triples
14 doubles
17 singles
14 walks
7 outs
12 sacrifices

_____

Working With Percents

A. Directions Rename these decimals as percents.

1) 0.16 = _____   5) 2.8 = _____   9) 0.01 = _____   13) 0.063 = _____

2) 0.05 = _____   6) 3.1 = _____   10) 4.56 = _____   14) 0.171 = _____

3) 0.017 = _____   7) 0.135 = _____   11) 7.8 = _____   15) 4.3 = _____

4) 13.1 = _____   8) 18 = _____   12) 2 = _____   16) 1.25 = _____

B. Directions Rename these fractions as percents. Show percents
rounded to the nearest tenth of a percent.

1) $\frac{3}{8}$ = _____   4) $\frac{6}{7}$ = _____   7) $\frac{2}{3}$ = _____   10) $\frac{6}{13}$ = _____

2) $\frac{5}{8}$ = _____   5) $\frac{1}{3}$ = _____   8) $\frac{11}{12}$ = _____   11) $\frac{4}{15}$ = _____

3) $\frac{3}{4}$ = _____   6) $\frac{2}{5}$ = _____   9) $\frac{3}{10}$ = _____   12) $\frac{1}{7}$ = _____

C. Directions Rename these percents as decimals.

1) 38% = _____   5) 226% = _____   9) 6% = _____   13) 0.03% = _____

2) 41% = _____   6) 8.2% = _____   10) 2.03% = _____   14) 105% = _____

3) 6% = _____   7) 9.22% = _____   11) 0.09% = _____   15) 1.94% = _____

4) 2.5% = _____   8) 13% = _____   12) 5% = _____   16) 3.2% = _____

D. Directions Rename these percents as fractions.

1) 11% = _____   5) 2.5% = _____   9) 77% = _____   13) 4% = _____

2) 6% = _____   6) 8.4% = _____   10) $3\frac{1}{3}$% = _____   14) 135% = _____

3) 10% = _____   7) 420% = _____   11) 1.4% = _____   15) 1% = _____

4) $12\frac{1}{2}$% = _____   8) 3% = _____   12) 7.12% = _____   16) 5.9% = _____

Write the Fraction

Directions Write the fraction that represents the shaded portion of each drawing. Express each fraction as a percent rounded to the nearest whole percent.

1)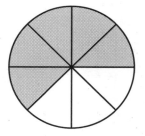

_____

2)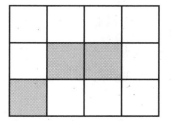

_____

3)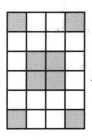

_____

4)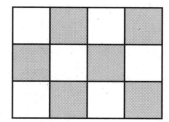

_____

5)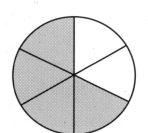

_____

6)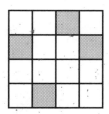

_____

7)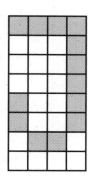

_____

8)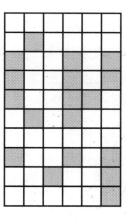

_____

9)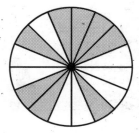

_____

Percent Sentences

A. Directions Find the rate. Rounding is not necessary.

1) _____ % of 6.6 is 0.132
2) _____ % of 20 is 1.6
3) _____ % of 7.3 is 0.73
4) _____ % of 6 is 1.08
5) _____ % of 6 is 1.8
6) _____ % of 25 is 2.25
7) _____ % of 2 is 1.6
8) _____ % of 200 is 112

9) _____ % of 38 is 1.14
10) _____ % of 3 is 2.85
11) _____ % of 0.83 is 0.3984
12) _____ % of 13 is 1.04
13) _____ % of 9 is 2.7
14) _____ % of 70 is 0.175
15) _____ % of 8 is 0.64
16) _____ % of 5.8 is 0.754

B. Directions Find the base. Rounding is not necessary.

1) 28% of _____ is 14
2) 60% of _____ is 54
3) 80% of _____ is 88
4) 75% of _____ is 37.5
5) 35% of _____ is 29.75
6) 8.1% of _____ is 4.05
7) 4% of _____ is 1.32
8) 7% of _____ is 0.161

9) 4.5% of _____ is 0.36
10) 9% of _____ is 0.144
11) 2% of _____ is 0.8
12) 120% of _____ is 4.2
13) 8% of _____ is 5.04
14) 10% of _____ is 7.3
15) 95% of _____ is 6.65
16) 30% of _____ is 6

C. Directions Find the percentage.

1) 23% of 63 is _____
2) 8% of 31 is _____
3) 4% of 35 is _____
4) 22% of 53 is _____
5) 6% of 90 is _____
6) 72% of 200 is _____
7) 3% of 200 is _____
8) 61% of 38 is _____

9) 53% of 1.61 is _____
10) 18% of 23.6 is _____
11) 9% of 4.8 is _____
12) 3.3% of 28 is _____
13) 80% of 50 is _____
14) 25% of 10 is _____
15) 150% of 72 is _____
16) 39% of 39 is _____

Installment Buying

Directions Complete these installment charts. Use a 2% finance charge.
Round all money to the nearest whole cent.

1)

Month	Previous Balance	Finance Charge	Before Payment	Monthly Payment	New Balance
Jan.	$200.00	——	$200.00	$75.00	$125.00
Feb.	$125.00	$2.50	$127.50	$75.00	$52.50
March					

2)

Month	Previous Balance	Finance Charge	Before Payment	Monthly Payment	New Balance
Jan.	$300.00	——	$300.00	$30.00	$270.00
Feb.	$270.00	$5.40			
March					
April					
May					
June					

3)

Month	Previous Balance	Finance Charge	Before Payment	Monthly Payment	New Balance
Jan.	$175.00	——	$175.00	$25.00	$150.00
Feb.					
March					
April					
May					
June					
July					
Aug.					

Shade the Portion

Directions Use your pencil to shade the portion of each drawing that represents the given value.

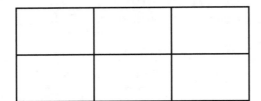

1) The shaded value is $\frac{5}{6}$.

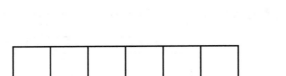

2) The shaded value is $\frac{7}{12}$.

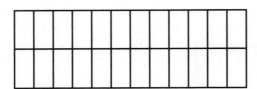

3) The shaded value is $\frac{11}{24}$.

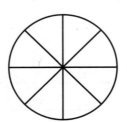

4) The shaded value is 75%.

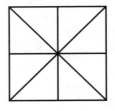

5) The shaded value is 75%.

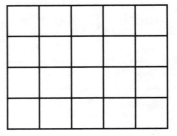

6) The shaded value is 85%.

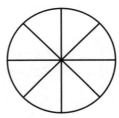

7) The shaded value is $\frac{5}{8}$.

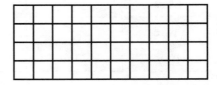

8) The shaded value is $\frac{5}{8}$.

Vocabulary Search for Chapters 12-14

Directions Here are 24 vocabulary words. Find each word in the puzzle.
The words go across, down, and diagonally.

Circle	Number	Slugging
Compound	Official	Spending
Decimal	Percentages	Statistics
Discount	Principal	Stolen
Games	Rate	Tax
Graph	Sacrifice	Totals
Interest	Sales	Triples
Loan	Simple	Walks

```
Z  S  D  B  J  J  S  G  C  N  E  E  I  E  V
T  P  R  J  L  E  A  E  N  C  V  G  G  C  S
H  E  Z  V  M  O  L  K  I  M  N  I  C  L  T
U  N  P  A  T  C  O  F  F  I  C  I  A  L  A
P  D  G  E  R  R  I  Y  G  L  H  T  R  T  T
R  I  D  I  R  R  I  G  N  P  O  E  S  C  I
I  N  C  X  C  C  U  P  A  T  B  E  L  O  S
N  G  U  A  O  L  E  R  L  M  R  A  S  M  T
C  V  S  F  S  V  G  N  U  E  M  G  I  P  I
I  D  I  S  C  O  U  N  T  I  S  S  M  O  C
P  S  T  O  L  E  N  N  C  A  K  Z  P  U  S
A  S  A  L  E  S  I  E  N  L  G  Y  L  N  N
L  U  C  L  T  L  D  A  A  A  Q  E  E  D  T
N  R  Y  G  R  A  O  W  V  W  E  R  S  W  L
Z  G  U  H  A  L  X  U  X  M  R  A  T  E  W
```

Auto Insurance

Age of Driver	Sex	Pleasure Use	Drives Less Than 10 mi. to Work	Drives 10 mi. or More to Work	Car Used for Work	Farm Use
17	M	1.80	1.90	2.20	2.30	1.55
	F	1.55	1.65	1.95	2.05	1.30
18	M	1.70	1.80	2.10	2.20	1.45
	F	1.40	1.50	1.80	1.90	1.15
19	M	1.60	1.70	2.00	2.10	1.35
	F	1.25	1.35	1.65	1.75	1.00
20	M	1.50	1.60	1.90	2.00	1.25
	F	1.10	1.20	1.50	1.60	.85

Directions Find each person's annual auto premium by multiplying the
basic premium by the appropriate factor from the table.

1) Elaine is 18 years old. She drives 6 miles to
work. Her basic premium is $176.

_____

2) Richard is 17 years old. He uses his car for
pleasure. His basic premium is $183.

_____

3) Roy drives 11 miles to work. He is 19 years
old. His basic premium is $192.

_____

4) Ben is 20 years old. He only drives on his
parents' farm. His basic premium is $204.

_____

5) Judith drives 7 miles to work. She is 18 years
old. Her basic premium is $188.

_____

6) Henry is 17 years old. He uses his car on his job
delivering pizzas. His basic premium is $181.

_____

7) Ron drives 14 miles to work. He is 20 years
old. His basic premium is $179.

_____

8) Marsha is 18 years old. She drives 3 miles to
work. Her basic premium is $216.

_____

Buying Hedge

Directions Find the cost of planting a hedge along the dark lines for each
property. Hedge costs $3.25 per yard.

1)
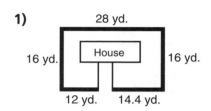
28 yd.
16 yd.   House   16 yd.
12 yd.   14.4 yd.

_____

5)
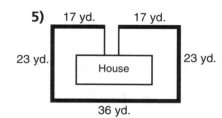
17 yd.   17 yd.
23 yd.   House   23 yd.
36 yd.

_____

9)
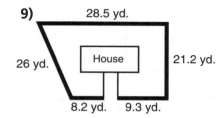
28.5 yd.
26 yd.   House   21.2 yd.
8.2 yd.   9.3 yd.

_____

2)
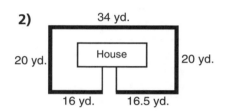
34 yd.
20 yd.   House   20 yd.
16 yd.   16.5 yd.

_____

6)
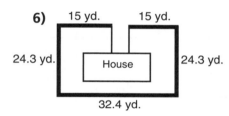
15 yd.   15 yd.
24.3 yd.   House   24.3 yd.
32.4 yd.

_____

10)
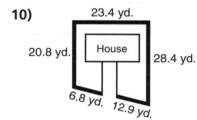
23.4 yd.
20.8 yd.   House   28.4 yd.
6.8 yd.   12.9 yd.

_____

3)
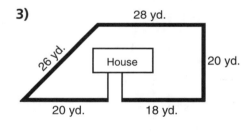
28 yd.
26 yd.   House   20 yd.
20 yd.   18 yd.

_____

7)
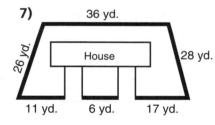
36 yd.
26 yd.   House   28 yd.
11 yd.   6 yd.   17 yd.

_____

11)
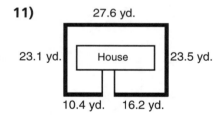
27.6 yd.
23.1 yd.   House   23.5 yd.
10.4 yd.   16.2 yd.

_____

4)
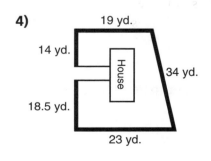
19 yd.
14 yd.   House   34 yd.
18.5 yd.
23 yd.

_____

8)
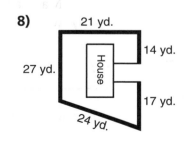
21 yd.
27 yd.   House   14 yd.
17 yd.
24 yd.

_____

12)
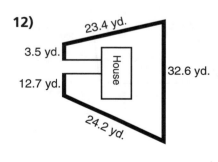
23.4 yd.
3.5 yd.   House   32.6 yd.
12.7 yd.
24.2 yd.

_____

Measuring in Centimeters

A. Directions Use a metric ruler. Find lengths of each line segment to the nearest tenth of a centimeter.

1) _____?_____ 2) _____?_____

3) _____?_____ 4) _____?_____

5) ____?____ 6) _____?_____ 7) _____?_____

8) _____?_____ 9) _____?_____

10) _____?_____ 11) _____?_____

12) _____?_____

13) _____?_____ 14) _____?_____

B. Directions Use a metric ruler to find the perimeter of each shape.

1)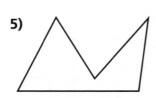

Perimeter = _____

2)

Perimeter = _____

3)

Perimeter = _____

4)

Perimeter = _____

5)

Perimeter = _____

6)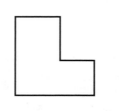

Perimeter = _____

7)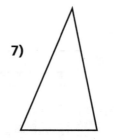

Perimeter = _____

8)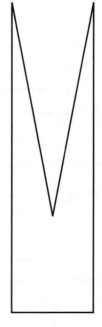

Perimeter = _____

Finding the Area

Directions The drawings represent lawns to be fertilized. Find the area of the shaded part for each drawing. Write your answer on the line.

1)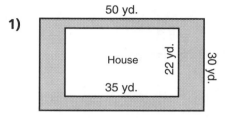

_____

2)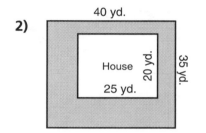

_____

3)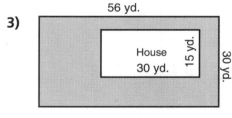

_____

4)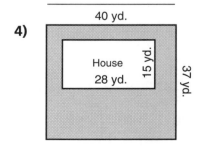

_____

5)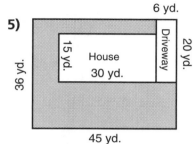

_____

6)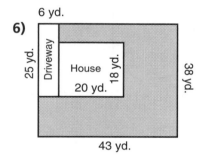

_____

7)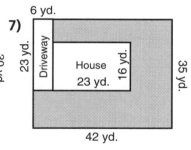

_____

8)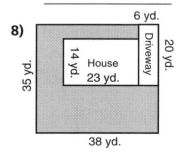

_____

9)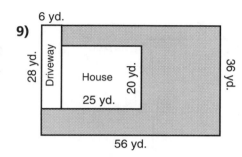

_____

10)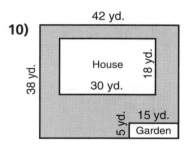

_____

11)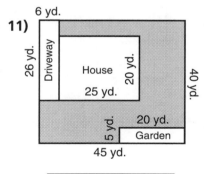

_____

12)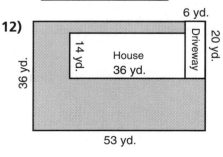

_____

Finding the Volume

Directions Write the volume for each rectangular prism.

1)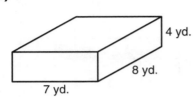
4 yd., 8 yd., 7 yd.

_____

2)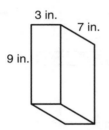
3 in., 7 in., 9 in.

_____

3)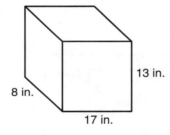
13 in., 8 in., 17 in.

_____

4)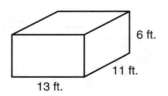
6 ft., 11 ft., 13 ft.

_____

5)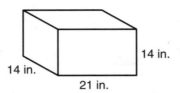
14 in., 14 in., 21 in.

_____

6)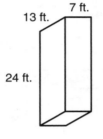
7 ft., 13 ft., 24 ft.

_____

7)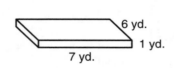
6 yd., 1 yd., 7 yd.

_____

8)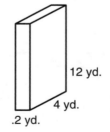
12 yd., 4 yd., .2 yd.

_____

9)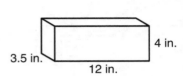
4 in., 3.5 in., 12 in.

_____

10)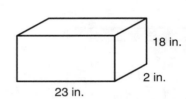
18 in., 2 in., 23 in.

_____

11)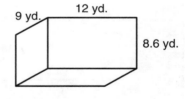
9 yd., 12 yd., 8.6 yd.

_____

12)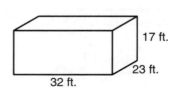
17 ft., 23 ft., 32 ft.

_____

Meters to Read and Mark

Directions Read these meters.

1) Reading: _____

2) Reading: _____

3) Reading: _____

4) Reading: _____

5) Reading: _____

6) Reading: _____

7) Reading: _____

8) Reading: _____

Directions Mark these meters.

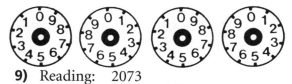

9) Reading: 2073

10) Reading: 3564

11) Reading: 3851

12) Reading: 0613

13) Reading: 1790

14) Reading: 5978

15) Reading: 6379

16) Reading: 2157

Celsius to Fahrenheit

Directions Convert the following Celsius temperatures to Fahrenheit.
Use the formula F $= \frac{9}{5} \times$ C $+ 32$. Round to one decimal place.

1) C $= 27°$ Fahrenheit $=$ _____

2) C $= 22°$ Fahrenheit $=$ _____

3) C $= 33°$ Fahrenheit $=$ _____

4) C $= 20°$ Fahrenheit $=$ _____

5) C $= 19°$ Fahrenheit $=$ _____

6) C $= 31°$ Fahrenheit $=$ _____

7) C $= 13°$ Fahrenheit $=$ _____

8) C $= 15°$ Fahrenheit $=$ _____

9) C $= 17°$ Fahrenheit $=$ _____

10) C $= 35°$ Fahrenheit $=$ _____

11) C $= 21°$ Fahrenheit $=$ _____

12) C $= 18°$ Fahrenheit $=$ _____

13) C $= 23°$ Fahrenheit $=$ _____

14) C $= 32°$ Fahrenheit $=$ _____

15) C $= 29°$ Fahrenheit $=$ _____

16) C $= 24°$ Fahrenheit $=$ _____

17) C $= 30°$ Fahrenheit $=$ _____

18) C $= 37°$ Fahrenheit $=$ _____

19) C $= 12°$ Fahrenheit $=$ _____

20) C $= 16°$ Fahrenheit $=$ _____

21) C $= 14°$ Fahrenheit $=$ _____

22) C $= 10°$ Fahrenheit $=$ _____

23) C $= 5°$ Fahrenheit $=$ _____

24) C $= 25°$ Fahrenheit $=$ _____

Fahrenheit to Celsius

Directions Convert the following Fahrenheit temperatures to Celsius.
Use the formula $C = \frac{5}{9} \times (F - 32)$. Round to one
decimal place.

1) F = 75° Celsius = _____

2) F = 48° Celsius = _____

3) F = 80° Celsius = _____

4) F = 34° Celsius = _____

5) F = 90° Celsius = _____

6) F = 56° Celsius = _____

7) F = 81° Celsius = _____

8) F = 85° Celsius = _____

9) F = 66° Celsius = _____

10) F = 88° Celsius = _____

11) F = 50° Celsius = _____

12) F = 55° Celsius = _____

13) F = 91° Celsius = _____

14) F = 93° Celsius = _____

15) F = 72° Celsius = _____

16) F = 79° Celsius = _____

17) F = 69° Celsius = _____

18) F = 68° Celsius = _____

19) F = 71° Celsius = _____

20) F = 72° Celsius = _____

21) F = 64° Celsius = _____

22) F = 65° Celsius = _____

23) F = 73° Celsius = _____

24) F = 89° Celsius = _____

Life Skills Math

Vocabulary Search for Chapters 15-17

Directions Here are 23 vocabulary words. Find each word in the puzzle. The words go across, down, and diagonally.

Auto	Fire	Perimeter
Celsius	Gas	Plan
Cost	Health	Polygon
Coverage	Insurance	Scale
Electric	Kilowatts	Term
Employee	Meter	Unit
Endowments	Month	Volume
Fahrenheit	Ordinary	

K	J	V	E	F	Y	T	E	H	J	L	F	M	C	E
F	I	W	E	H	S	F	N	M	E	T	E	R	C	M
E	G	C	W	O	F	T	D	U	L	V	T	N	V	Q
Q	J	K	C	P	I	V	O	D	Q	I	A	O	H	I
F	X	Y	H	O	F	Y	W	E	N	R	T	T	R	E
A	K	U	E	L	R	T	M	U	U	U	N	E	N	L
H	Z	I	A	Y	T	S	E	S	A	O	T	M	C	E
R	C	H	L	G	T	P	N	R	M	E	E	P	E	C
E	I	U	T	O	S	I	T	P	M	R	S	L	L	T
N	K	K	H	N	W	B	S	I	I	A	A	O	S	R
H	Y	G	S	G	N	A	R	F	G	C	H	Y	I	I
E	V	O	L	U	M	E	T	P	S	C	T	E	U	C
I	H	S	L	W	P	B	C	T	L	R	I	E	S	V
T	C	O	V	E	R	A	G	E	S	A	X	M	N	B
O	R	D	I	N	A	R	Y	K	X	A	N	L	M	D